images

illusion and reality

Adrien   Nude with flowers and shawl.   circa 1905

images
illusion and reality
Bede Morris

Australian Academy of Science
Canberra
1986

Typeset in 11/13 Meridian by
Jacaranda Publishing, Canberra, A.C.T.
Printed on 115 gsm Globlade by
Griffin Press Ltd, S.A.
Designed by Adrian Young, MSIAD
ANU Graphic Design.

Published by the
Australian Academy of Science,
G.P.O. Box 783
Canberra, ACT 2601

National Library Cataloguing in Publication Data

Morris, Bede.
   Images: illusion and reality.

   ISBN 0 85847 131 0.

   1. Photography — History. 2. Photography —
   Scientific applications. 3. Creative ability in science.
   4. Creation (Literary, artistic, etc.). 5. Art and science.
   I. Australian Academy of Science. II. Title.

770'.9

Cover illustration:
Computer-generated colour
pixel expansion from a detail of
Felix Nadar's 1860 collodion
print, *The hand of a banker; a
chirographic study* (pixel size
5 mm).

Preface

This book has been written as an accompaniment to the Art-Science exhibition "Images — Illusion and Reality" sponsored jointly by the Australian Academy of Science, the Academie des Sciences and the Société francaise de Photographie. The exhibition inaugurates a scientific and cultural exchange agreement between two Academies of vastly disparate ages: one founded by Jean Baptiste Colbert in 1666 and the other founded by a group of Australian scientists who petitioned Queen Elizabeth II for a Royal Charter in January 1954.

The exchange agreement between the two Academies was suggested by Professor Jean Bernard, Membre de l'Institut during his term as President of the Academie des Sciences. The idea of inaugurating the agreement with an exhibition of photography came from Professor Marcel Bessis, Membre de l'Institut. Through the good offices of Professor J.J. Trillat, Membre de l'Institut, President of the Société francaise de Photographie and Mme Christiane Roger, Deléguée Générale of the Société, an outstanding selection of rare photographic works of the Société was made available for the exhibition. The Australian Academy of Science added to this priceless historical collection, contemporary examples of photography to demonstrate the developments in this technology and the contributions it has made to science over the past 30 years.

The further purpose of the exhibition was to use photography as an example of the nexus between scientific discovery, art and human creativity and to put a case for science in these terms. Because scientific discoveries can be exploited by entrepreneurs to make money, the people who administer science are now preoccupied with ensuring that science funding comes with certain strings. These strings attach to accountability, cost-benefit and utility as defined by economists and politicians. Scientific research now has to be goal oriented, it has to address 'practical' issues and 'important' problems, it has to have a defined objective and a critical path. And so we have arrived at an era in science dominated by the administrator and the entrepreneur. Productivity and predictability are acknowledged before innovation and originality. The peer-reviewers reject the new hypothesis that is beyond their understanding in favour of the obvious and trivial out of a self-conscious adherence to public accountability. The delusion is complete and the ant-like activities of the measurers are applauded as the justification for scientific research.

In this climate, science and the creative scientist are extremely vulnerable. As Bessis says in his candid and perceptive essay, Science, Dreams and Poetry, "the creative scientist can never know exactly what he wants or know in any precise way, how to attain it. He remains, of necessity, in a miasma of uncertainty. He makes errors, falls into traps, takes enormous risks and may produce nothing definitive for months or years on end. His intellectual talents may dignify him as an enlightened man and yet finally, he must contend with the feelings of guilt associated with his unproductive efforts when he is judged by the measurers, the administrators and the contractors of research".

What peer review group would have recommended funding Nièpce in 1815 to do research on a method for producing pictures from elements of electromagnetic radiation, if he had claimed this research would lead to an analysis of the composition of the stars, a description of the internal machinery of cells, the form and structure of microbes and molecules, a method for diagnosing pregnancy by sound and cancers by radioactive imaging and, for good measure, the establishment of a motion picture industry, computerized tomographic brain scans, television and instantaneous news reports from around the world by satellite projection? Nièpce could never have been funded through a peer review system — all he had was a dream, an inspiration, a passion and a conviction. These sorts of things are for artists; they are not the stuff of discovery and certainly not a basis on which to fund research.

Many of the ideas and observations in this book came from Marcel Bessis and I have plagiarized them on the excuse that I have enjoyed many hours at Kremlin Bicêtre and at Planche Pigouche, discussing the philosophy of art and science with him.

The exhibition has been made possible by the French Embassy in Canberra and in particular, by the help of his Excellency M. Bernard Follin, the French Ambassador, the Cultural Attaché, M. Francis Josephe and the Cultural Councillor, M. Georges Zask. Professor Bessis,

Professor Bernard, Professor Trillat and Mme Roger have given much help in organizing the exhibition from Paris. I thank M. Giraudet, President, Fondation de France and M. Richon. UTA for their help in arranging the transport of the exhibition to Australia. In Australia, Professor A.J. Birch, President, Australian Academy of Science, Sir Ian Potter FAA, Dr R.W. Crompton FAA, Professor W.R. Levick, FAA, Dr W.J. Cliff, Dr Gutta Schoefl, Dr David Malin, Dr P. Hariharan, Alexander, Paula Dawson, Julian Eather, John Bruyn, Stuart Butterworth and Michael Dugan have helped very much with the manuscript and with the organization of the exhibition.

The design and production of this book and the catalogue for the exhibition have been done by Adrian Young, Graphic Designer, A.N.U., Mary Denton prepared the typescript and Sally Drumm and Wendy Trevella did the translations from the French.

The exhibition was brought to Australia by courtesy of UTA and its transport within Australia was by courtesy of TNT and TAA. The Academy is grateful to Mr D.M. Russo of Roadfast and Mr Gordon Smith of TAA for their very positive responses to the Academy's request for assistance. Other sponsorship for the exhibition has come from the Fondation de France, Kis Australia Pty Ltd, the Banque National de Paris, the Société Genérale and the Potter Foundation.

The Academy wishes to thank the Australian National University, the Anglo-Australian Telescope, CSIRO, Division of Entomology and the National Measurement Laboratory, the Australian Landsat Station, NASA Jet Propulsion Laboratories, the NSW Art Gallery, the National Library, the Queensland Art Gallery and the Victorian Museum for their contributions.

Bede Morris

Introduction

To see a World in a grain of sand,
And a Heaven in a wild flower,
Hold Infinity in the palm of your hand,
And Eternity in an hour.

The mystical romantic poet William Blake thus unwittingly expressed, far better than we can, the true feelings of creative scientists about the Universe, our World and our position in time. It is ironic that a poem entitled "Auguries of Innocence" should do this, since the practical results of science in creating our modern age are often now regarded as noxious, and destructive to basic human values.

It is not my purpose to argue this case, except to note that the understanding of the natural world, generated by scientific discovery and invention, can lead to the quasi-religious and mystical view of our Universe and ourselves as represented by Blake, and at the same time, at the behest of the exploiters and manipulators of practical outcomes, to the present benefits and disbenefits of our unique material civilisation. Science, as probably the most fundamental of all human activities, is not to be praised or blamed in this connection, but rather the attitudes of mind of those who employ its outcomes as tools.

What is quite certain is that after the last two hundred years of science, human attitudes to the past, the future and ourselves differ radically and permanently from those of any previous civilisation. The deep insight and knowledge conferred, the creative processes involved, result in so far unresolved tensions between the scientist as a creator of ideas and an intellectual, and the scientist as a progenitor of systems and technologies which are ambivalent in use in the hands of the community as a whole.

It is pleasing therefore to be able to look without reserve at the creation of images, in which scientific discovery and invention, together with artistic inspiration, have combined to record permanently the fleeting instant, the seen and the unseen worlds, against a background of space, dimension, time and human society.

I wish you, on behalf of the Fellows of the Australian Academy and of our colleagues in the French Academy of Sciences and the French Photographic Society, the same excitement, pleasure and insight which we have experienced in gathering, assembling and contemplating these exhibits.

Our gratitude is particularly due to la Société Francaise de Photographie, for risking, for our edification and enjoyment, their precious, irreplaceable and fragile archives, probably for the last time in public.

We hope it will be the first of many events in our Academy in which the aesthetics of science and its broad creative connections will be revealed.

Arthur Birch
President,
Australian Academy of Science

Images; illusion and reality

*It is curious that we look into mirrors throughout our
lives and yet may never question why we appear
through them, left-side reversed but the right way up. Is
the answer to the puzzle — the source of mirror
illusions — in the mirror or is it in ourselves?*
R.L. GREGORY

J.N. Nièpce
Set table
*Reproduction of a glass negative plate
coated with bitumen of Judeah.*
1822

Science and art have been seen as 'two cultures' distinguished by ideology and by ethic, technology and process. Science and the scientific method deal in rationality, deductive logic and objectivity. Art and artistic expression are based on passion, perception and prejudice. Science is concerned with the discovery of empirical facts about nature and in developing concepts to bring these facts into an intelligible theory to explain the reality of the natural world. Art, on the other hand, is the personal statement of an attitude towards something that is acknowledged as real. Art is subjective and personal; it may support the reality or deny it; science claims to be the reality.

The view which sets scientists and the scientific method apart from personality and prejudice is false and misrepresents the essentially creative nature of science and the way in which conceptual advances are made by scientists through the use of mental abstractions, hypothetical constructs and illusions. Science and art have a binding commonality in creative and interpretive

SOCIETE FRANCAISE DE PHOTOGRAPHIE

L.J.M. Daguerre
Inside an antique shop.
This is one of the earliest
Daguerreotypes and the first
successful photograph to be
published.
Daguerreotype
1837

thought, craftsmanship, technique and communication. Because science is a human activity it is, like art, exposed to personal bias and subjectivity. This can be a good thing, for novel ideas and creative approaches to the solution of difficult problems often come from intuitive or subjective thoughts. We know that artistic ideas appear in all sorts of circumstances; as inspirations in night or day dreams, as metaphors or sometimes as analogies of phenonema understood in other contexts. So too can scientific theories. While artists interpret life in figurative, representational or abstract shapes, scientists deduce its vital processes from the structures and forms on which it is based. Because the essence of life is in fact, form and structure, it is natural enough that both artistic and scientific interpretations of life are needed to know its meaning.

Artistic creation and scientific creation depend on precisely the same mechanisms even though the end results of the two processes are quite different. An artistic creation is of its nature evanescent whereas a scientific fact or

SOCIETE FRANCAISE DE PHOTOGRAPHIE

Jean Bernard Foucault
A bunch of grapes.
Daguerreotype
1844

a natural law is characterized by persistence, reproducibility and universality. The common requirement for creativity in both art and science is passion and enthusiasm and the reward, exhilaration and pleasure. Discovery and creativity cannot be ordered on demand or made to occur out of a sense of duty or compulsion, in spite of what politicans and administrators may think. Ideas develop from unstructured thoughts and dreams that are the basis of all inspiration.

What we know and understand about our natural world is built on images and shapes which are recorded, interpreted and imprinted in our brains as the result of the experiences we encounter throughout our lives. The capacity of the human mind to hold and recall experiences provides the crucial time reference on which our identities depend. Without this reference, without this capacity for memory, recall and reminiscence, we have no identity, no personality, no individuality; we are souls without a history, caught in the ever-present of a featureless timescape. But while our memory is the

SOCIETE FRANCAISE DE PHOTOGRAPHIE

source of our self, it is not just a mental identity card; it is also the reference point from which we derive a view on the reality of the world in which we live.

Our senses allow us to record those interactions with the environment that are essential in regulating our physiological behaviour. We select our food and our companions, we avoid unpleasant experiences and we seek emotional contentment through the senses of sight, taste, touch, smell and sound. Beyond the immediate physiological responses induced by these sensations, the mind conjures up an imagery through which these experiences can be recalled.

Whatever the nature of the experience, the memory of it is almost always evoked in terms of a pictorial symbolism because the primary sense of man is vision. An event seen, touched, smelled or tasted is stored within the archives of the brain with a pictorial association as a memory for subsequent reference. However, such images and the memory of them do not stand alone. What is seen and remembered is conditioned by what has been

SOCIETE FRANCAISE DE PHOTOGRAPHIE

Hippolyte Bayard
The Venus of Jean Goujon.
The proof of this photograph
was presented by Chevreul to
the Academie des Sciences in
July 1853.
Calotype
1840

SOCIETE FRANCAISE DE PHOTOGRAPHIE

Hippolyte Bayard
The Church of La Madeleine.
*Reproduction by Claudine Sudre
from original negative*
1842–1845

Left
Count Olympe Aguado
A view inside a room.
Daguerreotype
1851

seen and remembered before. While each experience changes the point of view of the viewer, each memory recalled is not the memory of the event alone but the memory of a memory. These memories are not fixed but are evolving over time within the mind in relation to other memories; fading, becoming more vivid, more fanciful, less urgent, more embellished, less accurate, more confused. We treasure our memories as accurate records of our past without being aware that our mind imposes a strict censorship on all viewpoints; this is crucial for any coherent record to be had of the environment with which we interact. We need to reject almost all of the potential information available to us about our surroundings in order to be able to use life's experience. Memories of events are manageable only because they are constructed on the most eclectic basis. Forgetting is a crucial part of remembering.

And we forget because we must
And not because we will.
Mathew Arnold.

Photographer unknown
The Panthéon.
Daguerreotype
circa 1840

IMAGES; ILLUSION AND REALITY

The anatomy and physiology of vision

Anatomize the eye: survey its structure and contrivance; and tell me, from your own feeling, if the idea of a contriver does not immediately flow in upon you with a force like that of a sensation.

Hume's Dialogues concerning Natural Religion.

The essential organ of vision is the eye. The eye consists of a transparent lens and an iris diaphragm through which light rays enter and are focused onto the retina which lines the inside of the back of the eye-ball. Within the retina are layers of specific photoreceptors; special nerve cells which connect with the optic nerve and through this nerve with the areas in the brain which process visual stimuli. The human eye is able to respond in terms of only two attributes of light, brightness and differences in colour. The brightness of light is governed by

Photographer unknown
The church of La Madeleine.
Daguerreotype
circa 1840

the intensity of the light-waves, while colour is a function of wavelength; physically the eye can discern only the intensity and the wavelength of light.

As light rays pass through the lens of the eye, they form an inverted image on the retina just as in a camera the lens focuses an inverted image onto the film. The retinal cells, called rods and cones because of their peculiar shapes, respond to the light, passing on an electrical signal first to bipolar nerve cells and then to ganglion cells whose axons make up the optic nerve.

Other cells in the retina link with adjacent nerve cells and regulate the activity of the rod and cone cells. The central part of the retina, the fovea, contains the highest concentration of photoreceptor cells and is the region where the visual image is perceived in its most refined detail.

The nerve axons of the ganglion cells pass along the optic nerve to two principal regions of the brain: to the superior colliculus in the more primitive brain stem and to the visual cortex through connecting links with other

SOCIETE FRANCAISE DE PHOTOGRAPHIE

nerve cells in the lateral geniculate nucleus of the cerebral cortex. This is not the end of the visual connections in the brain, however, for there are other complex nerve paths travelling to other areas of the cortex and elsewhere. It seems likely that the visual system of the cortex and the superior colliculus provide for different types of visual functions, at least in some species.

Visual perceptions do not necessarily only come from light patterns reaching the retina from without. The fascinating thing about vision is that the retina and the brain can be induced to generate patterns and visual images by a variety of non-optical stimuli. Electrical or mechanical stimulation of the eye or brain can readily produce visual sensations which are quite unrelated to the visual world so that we really cannot deny that some of what we see originates from within ourselves rather than from the environment around us. While the eye provides the brain with an analysis of the world in terms of the reflected, scattered and refracted patterns of light that come from objects, the images that we perceive are

Baron Louis Adolphe
Humbert de Molard
The bridge.
Calotype
1846

Left
Hippolyte Bayard
Fountain in the Square of Notre
Dame.
Reproduction by Claudine Sudre
from original negative
1842–1845

corrupted in terms of their reality. This is because the information supplied to the brain is transmitted and received as discrete signals in regard to both space and time.

The photons entering the pupil are reordered by refraction to produce a focused image which, while detailed and precise, is irretrievably softened by the diffraction effects of the pupil's finite aperture. Beyond the pupil the photoreceptors record a view with an essentially grainy quality determined by the form and structure of the cells of the retina. The quality of the recorded image is still further degraded as the message is conveyed through the optic nerve to the brain. Not only does the input from the vast number of photoreceptors in the retina have to be condensed into the many fewer channels of communication contained in the stalk of the optic nerve but the velocity of the message is also reduced from the speed of light to the speed of transmission of the nerve impulse. This stupendous devolution affects the way in which the image is presented to the

SOCIETE FRANCAISE DE PHOTOGRAPHIE

Photographer unknown
Portrait of a woman (tinted).
Daguerreotype
circa 1840

brain for its consideration. And yet in spite of these constraints imposed on the way the message is transmitted, the recorded view is not as you might expect, like a granular image appearing on a ground glass plate or like a visual rataplan similar to the flickering projections of an early silent 'movie' — the image is continuous, precise, perfect and detailed in every aspect.

What we see is clearly not reality but illusion — but the illusion inextricably interwoven with the reality. What we see can be said to be a representation of reality,

limited by the physiological capacity of the visual system to reconstruct the real image from the myriad of messages permeating the neural networks of the brain. While we know something about the way the visual impulse is generated in the eye and transmitted to the brain we know almost nothing about the way the

Meade brothers
A portrait of Daguerre.
Daguerreotype
1848

SOCIETE FRANCAISE DE PHOTOGRAPHIE

impulse is perceived by the brain. To picture a visual image as the portrayal of a picture on some magic, light-sensitive film in the brain, like a photographic record, is far too simplistic, for the perception is not in fact the reality.

Through our eyes we register, transmit and record within our memory store, tetrabytes of information during a lifetime, each remembered piece being recalled each time as a visual image of something seen perhaps years before and never seen again. The visual system has this extraordinary capacity to distinguish the patterns of light which characterize an object, a face or a scene and, having recognized this pattern, to record and store its essential detail for recreation at another time. The reality of the recalled image is an illusion, which like the reconstruction of a holographic image stored anonymously on a photographic plate, becomes visible when the reference laser beam reconstitutes the image in positive form from the unrecognizable interference pattern. While a photographic image is created by physical and

Photographer unknown
Woman in evening dress.
Daguerreotype
circa 1840

Photographer unknown
Mother and child.
Daguerreotype
circa 1840

chemical phenomena not all that different from the processes whereby a visual image is produced within the eye, a photograph is a non-interpretive image with a precise and immutable complement of information. The visual image is not like this at all, even at the moment in time when it is first recorded. The brain takes the visual image and interprets it in terms of past experience, present knowledge and future expectations.

The Perception of Reality

We know intuitively and objectively through the part science has played in expanding our knowledge of the cosmic and microscopic worlds, that we are physiologically incapable of perceiving anything but a miniscule amount of the real world or of comprehending it, even if it could be perceived. Our perceptions of the natural world are of course both real and illusory. The certainty of what is reality and what is illusion, however, is knowable only from points of reference that we accept as

SOCIETE FRANCAISE DE PHOTOGRAPHIE

Photographer unknown
Portrait of a women (tinted).
Daguerreotype
circa 1840

defining these two states. These references are not built into the germ-line cells as part of our genetic constitution; they are developed by culture and by experience and retained within our memory. A picture that is perceived and registered as a portrayal of some recognized reality by a person from a western culture might mean something entirely different to someone of tribal origin with a different background of experience. The visual image as represented in a drawing or photograph thus has no meaning in itself, it can only prompt an emotion. From this emotion the brain will infer the reality which the image represents. The reality of a subject thus lies hidden behind its image; the real subject cannot be seen, it can only be imagined. Unless there are previous experiences stored within the brain from which to imagine the reality, the image will convey either an

Photographer unknown
Man in Spanish costume.
Daguerreotype
circa 1840

unrecognizable or an ambiguous meaning. However, even when the image is recognized, it cannot convey a meaning with any precision. The aphorism that a picture is worth a thousand words is true, but only in regard to a description. The precise definition of the image requires a legend or caption to limit the viewer's range of possible interpretations; this holds as much for a work of art as it does for a photograph. Perception thus comes from inferences derived from data held within our visual memory coupled with instructions given to us when the image is presented. An illusion is created by errors in these inferences. Von Helmholtz, the German psychologist (1821–1890) wrote of illusions as 'the belief that we see such objects as would, under conditions of normal vision, produce the retinal image of which we are actually conscious'. Put simply we see and believe what we expect to see and believe.

Much of our natural world, which is unquestionably real, is unrecognizable in terms of our senses. Whilst our physiology restricts the appreciation of form and struc-

Hippolyte Bayard
Bayard in his garden.
Calotype
1842

ture to what we can see, science has allowed our understanding of the natural world to escape these physiological constraints. The paradox is that we can now recognize forms and structures that are in fact unrecognizable. Science has enabled the patterns produced when matter interacts with various sources of energy such as electron beams, X-rays, infra-red and ultra-violet rays, radio-waves, sound waves and so forth to be transmogrified into visual images. These are images of forms and structures which are invisible and unreal even though their existence is undoubted. The capacity to analyze structure and form through the visual interpretation of things which cannot be seen is a unique feature of our visual sensuality. We do not choose to interpret and analyze inaudible sound by making it audible; we do not choose to interpret and analyze tasteless sensations by making them tasteful any more than we try to appreciate the reality of textureless structure by changing its texture or a scentless flower by giving it a scent. The sensations of taste, sound, touch and smell

Hippolyte Bayard
The dray.
Reproduction by Claudine Sudre
from original negative
1842–1845

IMAGES; ILLUSION AND REALITY

have reality only within the dimensions of our immediate awareness. Beyond this these sensations are ineffective references unless they are coupled to an aspect of pictorial imagery.

This capacity of the human mind to create images defines not only the real world but the world of phantoms, of dreams, of nightmares, of inspirations, of poetry, art and music. Reality, however, is not defined only by sensual awareness any more than unreality is defined by metaphysical or abstract thought or by dreams and nightmares. The extension of our visual experiences and knowledge about other worlds of which we can have no awareness has compelled us to create pictorial illusions to understand and to communicate our perceptions of these worlds to others. Although science is seen as an exercise of objective and rational truth, scientific progress depends very much on a strategy based on illusion and supposition. Illusions are used to create hypotheses and to provide explanations of phenomena which later on may become an accepted version of truth incorporated

Hippolyte Bayard
The Café de France.
Reproduction by Claudine Sudre
from original negative
1842–1845

into our personal representation of the natural world. The illusion becomes the instrument by which further understanding and knowledge is derived and from which we learn of reality. The creation of these illusions or models is as crucial in the process of scientific discovery as it is in artistic expression.

Roger Fenton
Genre scene. Family in mourning.
Calotype 1855

While the scientist is concerned with the analysis of natural phenomena in objective terms, the artist seeks to interpret both the natural and metaphysical world in terms of emotions, feelings and aesthetic perceptions portrayed through a particular medium. The philosophy behind a work of art, the ideas, the intellectual message and the meaning are conditioned by the thoughts and aspirations of the artist. The technical possibilities for conveying these perceptions and aspirations have been influenced dramatically by scientific discoveries. This is

particularly illustrated in the discovery of the photographic process, the subsequent development of this science and technology and its incorporation into art. Before 1839 there was no possibility that artistic perceptions could find expression in the portrayal of shape, colour and texture in permanent recorded patterns of light and shade, let alone that 3 or 4 dimensional images of things unseeable or even non-existent could be transformed into visual works of art. But this is just what photography has meant to art and artistic expression.

Photography allows a moment in time to be recorded for posterity with astonishing accuracy and detail. A photographic record of an event thus differs from a painting or a memory of the same event in that it does not evolve or change in relation to time, it is not censored in terms of the detail of its content and its accuracy is completely vouchsafed. It is these characteristics that have made the photograph so valuable as a record and as a technique of scientific measurement while at the same time leading to its devaluation as an art form. The argu-

Hippolyte Bayard
The sulky child.
Reproduction by Claudine Sudre
from original negative
1842–1845

ment went like this. Artists paint what they see but they do so by interpreting the visual image; they use vision as an interpretive null instrument to learn and understand more about reality. In Emile Zola's terms art is 'la nature vue a travers un tempérament'. The photographer can only record the visual image, he cannot interpret it, so his artistic contribution can only come from composition, vantage and technical artistry. This is of course not true. Out of the quite primitive representations of images depicted in the first photographs has grown a variety of techniques for inscribing in black and white and in colour, not only the precise details of subjects but the artistic impressions and interpretations of these subjects; pastoral and urban scenes, portraits, natural phenomena, catastrophes, war, sports, fashion, natural history and so

C. Nègre
Composite scene of six prints.
The pipers, the women of Arles,
the chimney sweeps, the
stonemasons.
Calotype 1857

SOCIETE FRANCAISE DE PHOTOGRAPHIE

on. The development of new technologies in photographic materials, in lens construction and in optical physics and chemistry has given photography a sophistication and utility which have made it indispensible in science and communication and one of the greatest challenges for the creative artist.

Frederick Scott Archer
A view of Rochester.
Collodion (wet)
1857

IMAGES; ILLUSION AND REALITY

The history of photography

Light is that silent artist
Which without the aid of man
Designs on silver bright
Daguerre's immortal plan.
J.P. SIMONS

Camille Silvy
The Huidne river valley.
Collodion
1859

IMAGES; ILLUSION AND REALITY

Most discoveries have numerous claimants for proprietary of ownership and nationalistic sentiments often tend to pervert historical accuracy. Apart from this, science and scientific historians have a highly developed preoccupation with assigning the ownership of discoveries to particular individuals. Such a system, accepted and endorsed by science and the community, is bad in concept and very frequently incorrect in its conclusions. Science and the process of scientific discovery cannot proceed on the basis of discoveries by individuals; no one owns an idea. Science is part of civilization, and the civilizing process is not merely some minor aspect of personal career development or of the 'star' culture. While it may be possible to identify retrospectively a particular moment in history from which a discovery can be dated, the discovery itself has inevitably depended on other previous discoveries and ideas. Further, the merit of any of these ideas is unassessable except retrospectively in the context of the history of society.

C. Nègre
Two prints. The cocoa merchant
and a portrait of a farmer's wife.
Calotype
1851

IMAGES; ILLUSION AND REALITY

Events that occurred in the early eighteen hundreds focused attention on the development of ways of rendering permanent images with light and the remarkable possibilities this offered for exploitation in science, commerce and art. The discovery of photography depended on the previous development of two scientific ideas, the optical principles of image formation in an apparatus designated the 'camera obscura' and knowledge about the photochemical reaction that occurs when silver salts are exposed to light.

The camera obscura was an invention that had been known and used for hundreds of years prior to the 19th century. Aristotle was aware that light entering a pinhole aperture in the wall of a light-tight box produced an inverted image of a subject on the opposing wall and such an instrument was used by Arab scholars in the 10th century to observe astronomical phenomena related to the sun. The incorporation of a lens in place of the pin-hole of the camera obscura was also known to improve the sharpness and brightness of the image pro-

SOCIETE FRANCAISE DE PHOTOGRAPHIE

Hippolyte Bayard
The windmills of Montmartre
off the rue de Tholozé.
Reproduction by Claudine Sudre
from original negative
1842–1845

Hippolyte Bayard
The trellis.
Reproduction by Claudine Sudre
from original negative
1842–1845

jected on the wall of the box. The camera obscura was used in the 17th and 18th centuries for drafting, painting and copying various subjects such as anatomical specimens, buildings, maps, portraits and landscapes. This device and the ideas it incorporated became the basis of the camera which was used to produce the first photographic images.

The discovery of the photochemical reaction that occurs between silver salts and light was made by Johann Schultze, a German anatomist, in 1725. Schultze's discovery was confirmed by others, notably by the Italian, Giacomo Beccaria, the Englishman William Lewis and the Swede Carl Scheele. Scheele was the first to recognize that the blackening produced by the photochemical reaction of light on silver salts was due to the deposition of metallic silver. It was from this optical and photochemical base that the 19th century experimentalists began their quest for a method of producing permanent images formed by the action of light on a chemical substrate.

Photographer unknown
Portrait of a young woman.
Daguerrotype
1850

SOCIETE FRANCAISE DE PHOTOGRAPHIE

IMAGES; ILLUSION AND REALITY

If any one individual has a particular claim as the discoverer of photography it belongs to the Frenchman Joseph Nicéphore Nièpce; the subsequent development of the process was due to a collaboration between Nièpce and a compatriot, Louis Jacques Mandé Daguerre. Some other individuals who deserve more than an honourable mention for their contributions were Thomas Wedgwood of the famous English potter family, William Henry Fox Talbot, a scientist from Cambridge University and Hippolyte Bayard, a Paris civil servant.

The chronology of the discovery and development of photography from the early 19th century begins around 1800 when Thomas Wedgwood first showed that light patterns could be recorded on materials sensitized with silver nitrate. His demonstration of the potential of this photochemical reaction to register patterns of light intensity was highly original but his results stopped far short of his intention to produce a fixed, permanent image from the camera obscura. In the event Wedgwood was only able to record silhouettes of objects and not a

SOCIETE FRANCAISE DE PHOTOGRAPHIE

Victor Régnault
The son of Victor Régnault.
Reproduction by Claudine Sudre
from original negative
1850

focused camera image. He published his results through the good offices of his friend Humphrey Davy in the June 1802 issue of the Journal of the Royal Institution.

Nièpce, an amateur inventor who lived at Chalon-sur-Saône, knew of Wedgwood's experiments with silver salts in which light was used to produce images on treated leather, paper and stone. Nièpce's interest in lithography, a popular development at the time, led him to conduct experiments on ways of using light to effect lithographic copies on stone. He had the idea of placing a plate coated with a light sensitive substance within a camera obscura and recording on this plate the focused image entering through the pin-hole.

Nièpce's first experiments on photography were done with silver chloride or silver nitrate impregnated paper and coated metal plates in 1815. In these he was assisted and encouraged by his brother Claude. The first photographs that were produced were taken from the window of the family house in Gras. The pictures lacked definition and sharpness, and at this stage Nièpce's method

L.D. Blanquart-Evrard
Self-portrait.
Calotype
1847

SOCIETE FRANCAISE DE PHOTOGRAPHIE

L.D. Blanquart-Evrard
Portrait of two women.
Calotype
1847

SOCIETE FRANCAISE DE PHOTOGRAPHIE

gave results that were non-persistent and, of course, tonally reversed, i.e. negatives.

Nièpce recognized that a crucial deficiency in his photographic process was its inability to produce a positive representation of his subjects. He set about installing an objective lens in combination with a cardboard diaphragm in his camera obscura so that the light rays entering the lens could be more sharply focused on the sensitized plate at the rear of the chamber. He also saw quite clearly that it was essential for the successful

development of the process, to have adequate and permanent fixation of the recorded image on the plate. These early experiments of Nièpce, although technically very imperfect, were sufficiently promising for his brother Claude to raise the prospect of the theft of the

Victor Régnault
The park of Saint-Cloud.
Reproduction by Claudine Sudre from original negative
1850

intellectual property relating to the discovery and its commercial exploitation by a third party.

The first attempts by Nièpce at capturing an image with a silver chloride impregnated plate were followed in 1822 by a quite different set of experiments in which he used a type of asphalt, 'bitumen of Judea', as the photosensitive medium. This material has a differential solubility in lavender oil depending on the length of time it has been exposed to light and the intensity of the exposure. Nièpce coated glass and metal plates with the

bitumen dissolved in lavender oil and allowed these to dry. He then showed that when these plates were exposed to light either in the camera obscura or reflected from or transmitted through an object, an image of the light pattern was retained in the bitumen layer. The exposed bitumen became hard and insoluble while the unexposed material remained soft and could be dissolved away with lavender oil. Nièpce also showed that the metal plate could then be etched by mordant acid to give a permanent outline of the bitumen image in the

Photographer unknown
A View of Paris — The Arc de Triomphe.
Daguerreotype
circa 1840

SOCIETE FRANCAISE DE PHOTOGRAPHIE

metal. This procedure was termed héliogravure by Nièpce and is the basis of the photogravure process in use to this day. The most notable of these early photogravures was a portrait of Cardinal d'Amboise made by Nièpce in 1826.

Up to this time the images that Nièpce produced were heliographic copies of engravings; but in 1827 he produced a heliograph of an outdoor scene, the world's first photograph. It was a view from the window of his house taken across the courtyard showing a loft, a pear tree and the roof of a barn. Nièpce derived enormous personal satisfaction from this result and wrote to his brother indicating his desire to exploit the discovery commercially as soon as possible in case some pirate capitalized on the process. Nièpce was undoubtedly in need of finance to continue his experiments and saw the commercialization of his science as a means of obtaining funds for research — *Plus ça change plus c'est la même chose.*

Although these first photographs were enormously

SOCIETE FRANCAISE DE PHOTOGRAPHIE

Hippolyte Bayard
Place de la Concorde with the altar prepared for the commemorative service for those killed in the 1848 revolution.
Reproduction by Claudine Sudre from original negative

SOCIETE FRANCAISE DE PHOTOGRAPHIE

Photographer unknown
Changing the guard at the Tuilleries.
Daguerreotype
circa 1840

IMAGES; ILLUSION AND REALITY

exciting for Nièpce the images were imprecise and ill-defined. The very long exposure times blurred the outline of the subjects and eliminated the shadows as the sun moved across the field of view. Nièpce, however, was not about to concentrate on the defects of his results, he was delighted by the pictures, seeing them in terms of his inventive and artistic aspirations. It was hard to believe that within 10 years these rudimentary images would be transformed into pictures of incredible detail and fidelity.

Nièpce went to England shortly after he obtained his first heliogravure pictures in 1827 to visit his brother Claude who was very ill and living at Kew. While there Nièpce told Francis Bauer, of the Royal Botanic Gardens, about his discoveries. Bauer, who was a Fellow of the Royal Society, persuaded Nièpce to report his process to the Society and Nièpce wrote a note and forwarded it along with some examples of the heliographic process. The Royal Society did not publish his note and Nièpce's other attempts to interest possible patrons in England in

Paul Jeuffrain
Community kiln in Pompeii.
Reproduction by Claudine Sudre
from original negative
1852

Victor Régnault
Arcque la Bataille.
Reproduction by Claudine Sudre
from original negative
1850

his discovery met with no success. Nièpce returned to Paris disenchanted leaving behind his note to the Royal Society and various photographs with Francis Bauer.

On his return Nièpce met with Louis Mandé Daguerre in Paris. Sometime around 1825, Daguerre, a professional scene painter and showman, had begun to experiment with ways of producing images with light to avoid the laborious manual tracing of pictures produced by the camera obscura apparatus. Daguerre had heard of Nièpce's photographic experiments and wrote to him in 1826 suggesting a collaboration between the two. This collaboration had certain elements of exploitation by Daguerre of Nièpce's discoveries, for Daguerre at this time had nothing original to bring to the partnership. In spite of this inequality in the contributions of the two, the collaboration produced startling results in a short time. Nièpce died in 1833 but Daguerre continued the research and in 1835 discovered, almost certainly by chance, that when an exposed silver iodide plate was treated with mercury vapour, a perfect image of any light

Paul Jeuffrain
The basilica in Phaestos.
Reproduction by Claudine Sudre from original negative
1852

Paul Jeuffrain
Amphitheatre in Pompeii.
Reproduction by Claudine Sudre from original negative
1852

pattern that had fallen on the plate was revealed. The image could be stabilized by fixation in a solution of sodium thiosulphate. This was the basis of the process which Daguerre insisted on naming after himself even though he had a continuing contract of partnership with Nièpce's widow. Daguerre publicized the process all over Paris and achieved an extraordinary notoriety and public acclaim. Daguerre and Nièpce's son sold the proprietary rights of these remarkable discoveries to the French Government in return for life pensions and in Daguerre's case considerable fame and public and state recognition. The discovery was announced to the Paris press on 7th February 1839 by Francis Arago, a distinguised physicist, a member of the Academie des Sciences and a member of the French parliament. Arago presented the details of the discovery subsequently at a joint meeting of the Academie des Sciences and the Academie des Beaux-Arts on 19th August that same year, signifying both the scientific and artistic potentialities of the discovery. In introducing the discovery Arago used the term 'photo-

Paul Jeuffrain
The Port of Saerne in rain.
Reproduction by Claudine Sudre
from original negative
1852

graphie' to describe the process for the first time but unfortunately he made no mention of the capital contribution that Nièpce had made to the discovery. Francis Bauer, who still retained Nièpce's communication to the Royal Society written some years before, together with examples of his heliographic process, wrote to the Literary Gazette to correct this omission and to insist on an acknowledgement of Nièpce's part in the discovery.

While the photographic process developed by Daguerre during his collaboration with Nièpce gave an image of exquisite detail, the image could not be reproduced. As a consequence there were significant limitations to the commercial exploitation of the daguerreotype process which were recognized from the outset.

A Cambridge University chemist and Liberal political aspirant by the name of William Fox Talbot was also working on ideas for reproducing images by photo-chemical means at around the same time that Nièpce and Daguerre were collaborating on their experiments which led to the discovery of the Daguerreotype. There is

SOCIETE FRANCAISE DE PHOTOGRAPHIE

Paul Jeuffrain
Biskra.
Reproduction by Claudine Sudre
from original negative
1852

no doubt that Fox Talbot's ideas arose out of his background in chemistry quite independently of those of Nièpce and Daguerre, although it seems that they probably occurred to him somewhat later. Talbot, however, developed his photographic process from the outset as a means of obtaining a negative image from which any number of positive copies could be made. He impregnated paper sheets with silver chloride by alternately soaking the paper in a solution of brine followed by a solution of silver nitrate. After the image was produced in the paper by exposing it to light, the unreacted silver chloride was desensitized by soaking the paper in another salt solution. The negative image which resulted was then transformed into a positive by using a similar sensitized paper held in contact with the negative and then exposing the two sheets to light. Talbot became aware of the technique developed by Nièpce and Daguerre in January 1839, when Arago first announced their findings publicly in the press. To establish a claim for his own work Talbot submitted the details of his pro-

Victor Régnault
Dying child.
Reproduction by Claudine Sudre
from original negative
1850

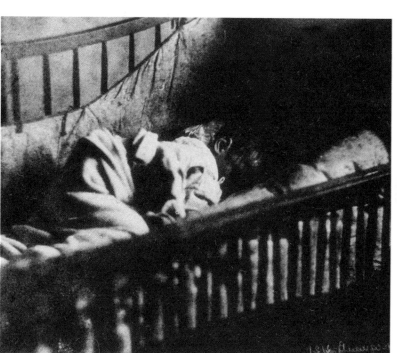

Victor Régnault
The grand-father and his grand-daughter.
Reproduction by Claudine Sudre
from original negative
1850

cess to the Royal Society in London not knowing whether his process was the same or different from that of Nièpce and Daguerre. He sent a copy of his paper to Arago in Paris at the time he submitted it to the Royal Society but it seems that this courtesy was not acknowledged.

When the details of the two photographic methods were published it was seen that they were essentially different in concept and process. The early Calotypes were aesthetically rather unsatisfactory and compared badly with the precise detail and definition of the Daguerreotype. Talbot patented his process in 1841 largely to enforce his personal claims over a discovery that was being mostly ignored in the blaze of acclamation and notoriety given to Daguerre at this time. Talbot and others, however, recognized the inherent flexibility of the negative process over the Daguerreotype positive. One of those who saw the potential of the negative-positive process was Hippolyte Bayard, a French public servant who was also experimenting with silver halide

SOCIETE FRANCAISE DE PHOTOGRAPHIE

Hippolyte Bayard
The bouquet.
Reproduction by Claudine Sudre
from original negative
1842–1845

impregnated papers around this time. He produced positive prints from paper negatives in June 1839. The details of Bayard's process were similar to those of Fox Talbot's although they were developed quite independently. Bayard reported his findings late in 1839 to the Academie des Sciences.

The beauty and detail of the early Daguerreotypes gave this process a widespread vogue compared to the much less perfect and more diffuse image produced from the textured paper of the early Calotype. However, the speed with which technical developments occurred with the Calotype was to be such that within twenty years of its pronouncement, the Daguerreotype was redundant and had been replaced by the negative-positive process. The exposure time required to produce an image on the early silver halide impregnated papers was very long, often a matter of many minutes. With the development of papers of increasing sensitivity and the recognition by Talbot that the latent image could be enhanced by chemical development, exposure times

Victor Régnault
Profile of Madame Régnault.
Reproduction by Claudine Sudre
from original negative
1850

Victor Régnault
Madame Régnault and her two
children.
Reproduction by Claudine Sudre
from original negative
1850

were soon dramatically reduced. This enormously increased the range of subjects and views which could be successfully recorded.

Within about 10 years of the invention of the Calotype, the development of collodion-coated glass plates impregnated with silver halide provided the stepping stone to photographic reproduction incorporating both the fidelity of the Daguerreotype and the reproducibility of the Calotype. New media to support the silver halide particles were being continually tested and

the collodion process was produced in 1851 by Frederick Scott Archer in England. While it represented a great advance over the impregnated papers on which Calotypes were produced, the dry collodion film was impervious to water and it had to be prepared, used and processed as a wet plate. These constraints were overcome with the major technical advance of incorporating the silver halide in a solution of gelatin which could be spread as a thin layer on the glass plates. Dry plates were soon prepared commercially and they presented to the

Baron Louis Adolphe
Humbert de Molard
Study of a country woman.
Calotype
1846

Victor Régnault
Madame Régnault.
Reproduction by Claudine Sudre
from original negative
1850

user all the conveniences of the modern day photographic materials. The sensitivity of the gelatin emulsion plate was much greater than the collodion plate and with this, exposure times could be made short enough to arrest moving subjects.

The range of scientific and artistic possibilities offered by the technical advances in plate and film preparation were enormous, but even more importantly the convenience of the new materials encouraged a wide interest in photography and it was used by an ever increasing number of amateurs as well as professionals. This popular use was further promoted by the invention of the Kodak camera by George Eastman in 1888. This camera used a roll of sensitized celluloid film on which a series of exposures was made, the roll being developed and printed by the manufacturer. Inconvenience no longer inhibited picture taking.

The development of photography in its earliest years was confined to black and white images although Nièpce had thought about reproducing images in natural

Victor Régnault
Madame Régnault and her
daughter.
Reproduction by Claudine Sudre
from original negative
1850

colour almost from the start of his early experiments. Variations in the black and white image were created by altering the colour of the emulsion layer on plates and by tinting the developed image with coloured dyes. Early attempts by Bequerel (1848) and Nièpce St Victor (1852) succeeded in producing coloured images on specially treated plates coated with silver chloride but these images were evanescent and could not be fixed. In 1861 James Maxwell demonstrated that combination images made in red, green and blue light could be used to re-produce a colour photograph by an additive principle. Louis Ducos du Hauron and Charles Cros independently developed the subtractive process of colour separation in which negatives made in red, green and blue light were converted into their complementary colours, cyan, magenta and yellow to produce a natural coloured posi-tive. It was Ducos du Hauron's experiences in mixing paints as a practising artist that made him aware that the appropriate proportions of blue-red, blue-green and yellow paint mixed together could provide almost any

SOCIETE FRANCAISE DE PHOTOGRAPHIE

Victor Régnault
The Régnault children.
Reproduction by Claudine Sudre
from original negative
1850

required colour. From these experiences and inspired by Maxwell's work he conceived the idea of superimposing in registration, dyed images of a single subject to produce a photograph in natural colour. Essentially the same idea was proposed by Charles Cros at the same time. The considerable efforts by many researchers to find a means of directly fixing coloured images in film with dye couplers led eventually to the commercial colour photographic process described as Kodachrome. This depended on the chromogenic conversion of a latent silver image directly into a colour image. The Kodachrome process was based on the separate development of colour images in a film which contained 3 emulsions of different colour sensitivity coated on the same base.

The Science and Technology of Photography

Photography is now so commonplace and is used by so many people that we scarcely stop to think of the science on which the technology is based. While the term itself usually refers to the production of a permanent image

Baron Louis Adolphe
Humbert de Molard
Double Print. Two groups of
people.
Calotype
1849

SOCIETE FRANCAISE DE PHOTOGRAPHIE

The chess players

The card players

produced by visible light, we recognize that the photographic process can now be used to record images from radiation of many different wavelengths in the electromagnetic spectrum as well as visible light.

The first pictures were taken by Nièpce with a homemade camera obscura into which a lens tube had been fitted. Nièpce acquired a professionally made camera from the Paris optical firm Chevalier, in 1826. These early cameras were of variable size but the most common dimension was around 15 x 20cm. The camera mostly used by Daguerre was an engine which weighed around 20kg. It consisted of two boxes which could be moved one within the other. The development of much smaller cameras and emulsions of high sensitivity to light together allowed short exposures to be made with hand held cameras as early as the 1860s. The improved mathematical formulation and design of lenses also allowed for much more versatility and much greater flexibility in the use of cameras and in the selection of subjects.

Baron Louis Adolphe
Humbert de Molard
The little chimney-sweeps.
Calotype
1846

In the production of the black and white negative-positive image, the reflected light from the subject passes through the lens onto the silver halide plate or film. The depth of focus and the amount of light that is projected onto the film as a focused image is controlled by the area of the lens exposed to light. The area is varied by opening or closing the diaphragm associated with the lens. Within the emulsion the photochemical reaction leads to the formation of an unseen image which can be intensified by chemical development and fixed by removing the unexposed silver halides. The amount of light impinging on the silver halide layer determines the amount of metallic silver produced by development, the blackest areas of the film representing the light areas of the subject. The changes that occur in the crystals of silver halide on exposure to light are quite undetectable before development.

A conventional photographic emulsion is comprised of myriads of crystal aggregates of silver bromide, silver iodide and silver chloride in various proportions.

L.A. & A.R. Bisson
The cathedral of Notre Dame.
Collodion
1849

Jacob August Lorent
Café des platanes in Algeria.
Calotype
1858

SOCIETE FRANCAISE DE PHOTOGRAPHIE

SOCIETE FRANCAISE DE PHOTOGRAPHIE

IMAGES; ILLUSION AND REALITY

Photochemical theory suggests that there are miniscule particles of silver metal incorporated into the silver halide crystals which act as 'sensitivity spots'. Electrons are released from the silver halide by the absorption of light energy and these migrate to the silver particles in the crystals giving them a negative charge. Silver ions are attracted to the negatively charged silver particles as in a microscopic electroplating process. When the silver grains reach a critical size, the developer reacts with them reducing the entire halide crystal to metallic silver.

The film is then fixed to remove the unexposed silver halide from the gelatin film and to harden it. This is done by the use of a fixing and hardening solution which usually contains sodium thiosulphate, sodium sulphite, acetic acid and chrome alum. A positive image is subsequently produced by simply re-photographing the negative on a similar light sensitive film or paper.

Roger Fenton
Rivault abbey.
Calotype
1859

This is done either by contact printing or with a projector or enlarger. The latent positive image is again developed and fixed in essentially the same way as for the negative image.

The development of colour images depends on the treatment of three superimposed sensitive emulsion layers to convert the latent images they contain into separate dyed images in the three subtractive primary colours, yellow, magenta and cyan in the correct intensities. The colour separation can be achieved either by the additive process discovered by Maxwell or the subtractive process described originally by Ducos du Huron and Charles Cros. In the additive process the synthesis of different colours is effected by combinations of coloured light to give the three primary colours. The subtractive synthetic process depends on the elimination of certain parts of the visible spectrum by appropriate filters. This latter process is the one on which most contemporary colour reproductions are based.

Colour film can give a positive colour image by a

J.M. Taupenot
Gymnasts from the military school, Prytanée de la Flèche.
Collodion (albuminized)
1855

SOCIETE FRANCAISE DE PHOTOGRAPHIE

L.A. & A.R. Bisson
Climbing Mont Blanc.
A traverse by horizontal ladder.
Collodion
1862

SOCIETE FRANCAISE DE PHOTOGRAPHIE

reversal process or by printing from a negative. The reversal film has three sensitized layers of emulsion, each one reacting specifically to the primary colour components of the image. During processing the dye in the respective layers is developed to produce a positive colour image complementary to the colour sensitivity of the emulsion; so called reversal processing. The final colour range on the transparency is due to the combination of the three subtractive primary colours in varying degrees of optical density to give a positive image. The

negative colour films produce their negative images directly through the development of the dye in the different emulsion layers. The resultant negative therefore substitutes a yellow negative image for blue, a cyan image for red and a magenta image for green. The authentic colours of the subject are restored in the positive printing process analogous to the black and white negative-positive method.

The chemical reactions involved in colour film development are quite complex. With reversal film the

Farnham Maxwell Lyte
The Scia bridge.
Collodion
1863

The Imperial Printery of Vienna
Am Hoff Square in Vienna.
Collodion
1857

first development step produces the negative image in each of the sensitive layers by reduction of the silver halide. This development is restricted beyond a certain point and the silver negative image is then bleached away. The film is then uniformly exposed to light to allow the residual silver halide to react — the film is in fact deliberately fogged. The second positive image is colour developed by the introduction of dyes and then treated with a second bleach bath to remove the silver images. The remaining silver halide is removed from the film by fixation so that only the 3 separate positive dyed images remain.

The application of the photographic process now extends throughout many areas of science and society. Specialized technology has been developed to enable photographs to be taken and printed instantaneously (the Polaroid process) and to transform almost any part of the electromagnetic spectrum into a visible image. High speed photography systems have been developed with stroboscopic flash lighting so that exposures of one

G.B. Gething
Workers in an English foundry.
Collodion (wet)
1857

SOCIETE FRANCAISE DE PHOTOGRAPHIE

millionth of a second or shorter can be taken. Photographs can be taken in air or under water, with sound waves, x-rays, radio waves or electron beams to record either the most miniscule or the most magniscule.

It would be impossible to assess the contribution that photography has made to human civilization or to know what effects it will have in the future. It is a process that has touched all our lives, be it at the Saturday movie matinee, or through the pleasure of a candid snapshot that acts as a reminder of some special moment, or as knowledge recorded for future generations in the pictures of the planetary space probes. It seems unlikely that either Nièpce, Daguerre or Talbot would have understood just how significant their first rudimentary images were and certainly they would not have thought that in 150 years time, photographs would be telling us something about the make-up of things as exotic and different as Halley's Comet, the eye of a cricket and the insulin molecule.

SOCIETE FRANCAISE DE PHOTOGRAPHIE

Champion
Mr & Mrs Ning Po.
Collodion
1866

SOCIETE FRANCAISE DE PHOTOGRAPHIE

Champion
A Market in Peking.
Collodion
1866

Photography and art

SOCIETE FRANCAISE DE PHOTOGRAPHIE

J. Schaeffer
Portrait of an old man from
Alsace.
Collodion
1857

IMAGES; ILLUSION AND REALITY

The early lilies became part of this child,
And grass, and white and red morning-glories, and white
*   and red clover, and the song of the phoebe-bird,*
And the fish suspending themselves so curiously below there —
*   and the beautiful curious liquid,*
And the water-plants with their graceful flat heads —
*   all became part of him.*
WALT WHITMAN, Assimilation

John Stewart
Portrait of John Herschel —
English scholar, 1792–1871.
Collodion
1856

John Stewart
Portrait of a young girl.
Collodion
1856

IMAGES; ILLUSION AND REALITY

Photography is now such a universally available technique that every camera enthusiast has become a potential artist and every photograph, a potential masterpiece. As a technology and art form, photography has had a pervasive effect on human civilization, influencing social evolution, education, science, culture and commerce as well as the artistic and aesthetic interpretation of the world. The early photographers used their cameras to record landscapes, monuments, buildings, scenes and personalities as a means of informing and instructing people about countries and civilizations remote from their own. Indeed it was Fox Talbot's personal ambition to record his own holiday travels through Europe that stimulated him to investigate ways of producing permanent pictorial records of his trips. As soon as it became possible to take photographs with exposure times as short as a few seconds or less, photographic portraiture became the rage. The early stylistic adaptations of portrait photography concentrated on the presentation of pictures of

SOCIÉTÉ FRANÇAISE DE PHOTOGRAPHIE

Charles Migurski
Soldier with a wooden leg.
Collodion
1860

SOCIÉTÉ FRANÇAISE DE PHOTOGRAPHIE

Charles Migurski
Portrait of a painter.
Collodion
1860

the notorious and newsworthy, on social records of the wedding and the christening, and on portraits destined for the family album. However by the 1850's technical developments had begun to take photography outside the photographic studio and into the realms of photo-journalism and communication. Photography was soon to become a news and information medium and society was captivated by the reality, interest and urgency of photographic reports of events geographically divorced from domestic life.

Beyond the recording of events, wars and catastrophes, photo-journalism soon entered the world of publicity, advertising and promotion, of industry, architecture, fashion and design and of course, the worlds of sport and entertainment. But while photography was capturing the public imagination as a technical substitute for pic-

Alphonse Riout
Portrait of a man.
Collodion
1857

torial memory and reminiscence, groups of artists were forming themselves into clubs and societies to promote the new technology as an art form and as a means of artistic expression. The first of these societies was formed by Colonel B.R. de Montfort in Paris in 1851, under the name of the Société Héliographique. There were around 40 foundation members of the Heliographic Society and its President was the very aristocratic Baron Gros. The artistic and scientific credentials of the Society were well founded in a membership which comprised the photographers Bayard, Le Secq, Le Gray and others, painters such as Delacroix, the scientists Becquerel and Régnault, writers like Champfleury and nobility like Count Aguado, Vicomte Vigier, Baron de Montesquieu and of course its President Baron Gros. The Société francaise de Photographie was formed in 1854, subsuming the

Louis Rousseau
Portrait of an army officer in the
Japanese Embassy of Tascoume.
Collodion
1864

SOCIETE FRANCAISE DE PHOTOGRAPHIE

Heliographic Society and taking over its membership. The first President was the distinguished scientist Henri Victor Régnault.

Other societies were formed in other countries to promote the science and art of photography and many of these became associated with particular artistic movements and technical developments in photography. The Photographic Society was formed in England in 1853 and its first President was Sir Charles Eastlake. Eastlake's artistic credentials were impeccable as he was also Presi-

dent of the Royal Academy at that time. He insisted, from the outset, in establishing *a prior* concepts of photography and defining its formal relationships to art. Coteries of photographers came together in England to promote mutual interests and ideas in photography and as a result the Camera Club of London, The Linked Ring Society, and later on, the Royal Photographic Society

Charles Migurski
Portrait of a man.
Collodion 1860

SOCIETE FRANCAISE DE PHOTOGRAPHIE

were established. In France, the Photo Club of Paris was founded by Puyo and Demachy in 1890 and became one of the centres of the 'pictorialist' movement in photography in Europe for the next 20 years. In the USA the Camera Club of New York was established in 1890 and later in 1902 the Photo-Secession Group was founded by Alfred Stieglitz as an offshoot of the Camera Club.

In its earliest phase of development, photography was seen as a perfect substitute for the craft of draftmanship; this was natural enough, given the origins of photography from the camera obscura. Daguerre was intent on using photography initially to provide the fidelity of line and detail he needed to make his Diorama productions more realistic. It was however the accuracy and detail of the photographic reproduction that seemed at first, to deny an interpretive dimension to the photographer. Photographs were just too vividly real to qualify as art. It was soon realised though by some photographers that the constraints of realism and detail were not necessarily draw-backs to the aesthetic presentation of an image nor

A. Personnaz
Winter landscape.
Carbon shadowing technique with Lumière autochrome plates
circa 1905

SOCIETE FRANCAISE DE PHOTOGRAPHIE

G. & R. Alinari
Soirée by lamplight. Print dedicated to Paul Nadar by the photographers.
Tinted carbon
circa 1900

SOCIETE FRANCAISE DE PHOTOGRAPHIE

did they necessarily restrict the photographer's creative role or his opportunity for social comment. Admittedly it seemed more difficult to express and interpret subjective perceptions in a photograph when the photograph itself so clearly represented the visual reality. But as photographic technology improved, the photographer found an undreamed of range of technical artifices with which to portray his aesthetic and artistic interpretations, almost as an instantaneous reaction. The interesting thing is that while the strictly scientific and technical nature of the photographic process might well have imposed restrictions on artistic expression, it turned out not to do so. The significant scientific advances in photochemistry, optical physics, colloid science, lens technology and so forth over the 150 years since photography was first discovered, far from overwhelming

Auguste Bertsch
Passing through the gate at the barrière Blanche.
Collodion 1855

photographic artists, have been taken for granted by them and used to further their artistic and photographic interpretations.

A. and L. Lumière
'The first experiments in Autochrome'.
Autochrome
1904

Portraiture

The earliest photographs were taken of still life, views from nature and subjects that were fixed or immobile. This was necessary because the technical limitations of film speed and lens construction required exposure times of the order of many minutes to produce the latent image. Artistic expression was consequently limited for the most part to subject selection, to composition and to vantage. As film speeds increased, portraiture of living subjects and candid snapshots became possible. Human

vanity being what it is, the similitude of the photograph often set the portrait photographer against his subject. When Queen Victoria asked the society photographer, Alfred Chalon whether he thought the painted portrait would be replaced by the photograph, he replied that this was unlikely because it was more difficult to flatter the sitter with a camera than with a paint brush. While people wanted a likeness, they wanted an imagined likeness and were often offended by the accuracy and detail of the photograph. The Daguerreotype however had such

stunning novelty and appeal that within a few years of its presentation to the world, an extensive industry had been built up around this process.

The early daguerreotype portraits were mostly presented around a stereotyped pose in a stereotyped cadre. Soon however, more adventurous photographers began to exploit the inherent accuracy of the photograph to introduce realism into portraiture, showing their subjects literally with their photographic warts and all. Whilst the crispness and detail of the Daguerreotype

SOCIETE FRANCAISE DE PHOTOGRAPHIE

L.D. Dufay
Still life of fruit.
Colour line screen method to produce natural colour
date unknown

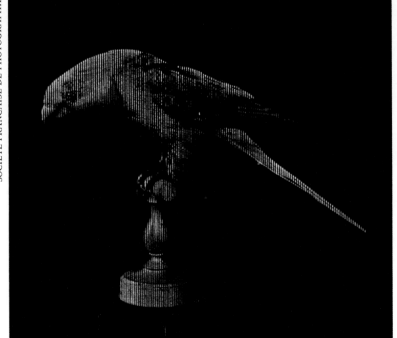

SOCIETE FRANCAISE DE PHOTOGRAPHIE

C.J. Joly
Parrot.
Colour line screen method to produce natural colour
date unknown

gave a quite uncompromising portrait, the Calotype had certain elements to it that were more easily exploited to give an image that was a good deal softer, less defined, and more 'arty' than the precise Daguerreotype; as a consequence the Calotype was thought to be more aesthetically appealing. The portrait photographs produced up until around 1850 and even later, were dominated by the style of contemporary oil painting, for photographic art was still very much derivitized on painting. Classical portraits by the English photographer Robert Adamson (1821–1848) done in collaboration with the painter David Octavius Hill, had a subject pose and composition quite like the paintings that were being exhibited in the Royal Academy at the same time. It was however not all one-sided as members of the Royal Academy at this time, had begun copying their portraits from Calotype photographs rather than from sitting subjects.

A significant development in portrait photography came from the development, by the French

A. Personnaz
Morning frost.
Carbon shadowing technique with
Lumière autochrome plate
circa 1905

IMAGES; ILLUSION AND REALITY

photographer Disdéri in the eighteen fifties, of the *carte de visite*. The idea of this photographic format was probably due to considerations of commerce and convenience rather than to any particular artistic or aesthetic pretensions. The *carte de viste* was a photograph 10 x 6 centimetres in size which was produced as multiples of 8 negatives on the one glass plate. In some respects these photographs foreshadowed the identity card or passport photograph of today except that *carte de visite* portraits were conceived as artistic works, something very few passport photos have ever aspired to. The style of the photographs was stereotyped with standard poses and props mostly conveying baroque and ornate papier mâché or material backdrops of castles, ballustrades and columns, with velvet drapes and tasselled drawcords.

A. Personnaz
Country landscape.
Carbon shadowing technique with
Lumière autochrome plate
circa 1905

A. Personnaz
Ploughing the field — Ile de
France.
Carbon shadowing technique with
Lumière autochrome plate
circa 1905

SOCIETE FRANCAISE DE PHOTOGRAPHIE

SOCIETE FRANCAISE DE PHOTOGRAPHIE

IMAGES; ILLUSION AND REALITY

The pictures were usually decorated by a variety of retouching and colouring procedures to make them as similar to paintings as possible.

Some photographers rejected the photographic imitation of painted portraiture and developed their own personalized styles. Gaspard Félix Tournachon (1820– 1910) the Frenchman who worked under the professional pseudonym of Nadar and the English-woman Julia Margaret Cameron (1815–1879) eschewed photographic conventions of the day and produced portraits of great artistic quality. Nadar's portrait work was recognized quite early on for its interpretive qualities and was acknowledged by the Academy des Beaux-Arts and featured in the leading and most influential illustrated magazines of the time. Nadar's portraits had a power and style which showed the emotional and

Gustave Le Gray
Sailboat returning to port.
Collodion
1857

intellectual qualities of both the subject and the photographer. Julia Cameron's accomplishments were no less impressive particularly when evaluated within the social context of the day. She was the wife of a civil servant who took up photography as a hobby. Her felicitous and privileged social background put her in contact with many celebrated contemporary English writers, scientists and artists. Although some of her pictures had certain technical defects of focus and exposure, she portrayed her subjects with insight and sensitivity. Mrs Cameron was preoccupied with the beautiful and the pristine and was much influenced in her work by the admiration she had for Raphael, Michelangelo and the Old Masters. Many of her compositional photographs now appear pretentious and sentimental in their message and statement but in the mid-Victorian context, they were seen as the pictorial equivalents of Tennyson's poetry and Rosetti's paintings.

The influence of painting on photography and photographic portraiture continued to impede the

SOCIETE FRANCAISE DE PHOTOGRAPHIE

Adrien
An outing by car.
Carbon shadowing technique with
Lumière autochrome plate
circa 1905

IMAGES; ILLUSION AND REALITY

establishment of an artistic identity for photography for many years. By setting down ground rules for photographic art based on painting, it was impossible for photographers to do other than attempt to formulate their pictures 'in accordance with the acknowledged principles of Fine Art'. Some of these principles were expressed rather heroically by photographers such as Oscar Rejlander (1813–1875) and Henry Peach Robinson (1830–1901). They presented allegorical themes and social commentaries as composite photographs constructed from multiple negatives. Pictorial representations were made of intimate human events that had only previously been portrayed by painters as abstractions. The community for which Robinson, Rejlander and Julia Cameron produced their photographic allegories looked for moral and ethical

Oscar-Gustave Rejlander
Portrait of Lionel Tennyson.
Collodion
1856

SOCIETE FRANCAISE DE PHOTOGRAPHIE

comment from artists on themes that would direct society towards the acknowledged goals of civilization. Rejlander's portrayal of the temptations to which youth is subjected in his allegorical masterpiece 'The two ways of life' is so attractively seductive that the viewer experiences a nostalgic surging within the loins that almost guarantees the rejection of any of the finer aspirations of life.

Both Rejlander and Robinson had been trained as artists before they took up photography and their photo-graphs demonstrate the interpretive constraints this training placed on their use of photographic verism. Robinson published a book entitled *Pictorial effect in photography* in which he set out in a series of rules and codicils, his formulation for artistic success in photography. Instructions were given for subject

Henry Peach Robinson
Young musician.
Collodion
1859

compostion and scene arrangement, posing procedures and so forth, based on painting techniques. Robinson's intellectual approach to photography and his 'pictorialist' view of its artistic potential, led to the production of photographs distinguished for their artificiality rather than for their perceptiveness or realism. These photographs desensitized the viewer's perception of reality by using synthetic scenes and by manipulating the photograph itself with dark room techniques to produce what amounted to camera representations of art. However by the 1870's the strength of photographic expression was already evident in its developing use in photo-journalism. Roger Fenton's photographic reports of the Crimean War were a first-time visual record of a battle so far from England that its conduct and outcome would have been expressed before photography in dispatches detailing the glory of a war justly fought for king and country. The explicit truth of the photographs of the Crimean and American civil wars changed the public perception of war forever. Prior to photography the pictorial represen-

SOCIETE FRANCAISE DE PHOTOGRAPHIE

Félix Nadar
Portrait of Francois Millet,
landscape painter, 1815–1875.
Collodion
1856

tation of war was in the artistic extravaganzas of Delacroix and David. Photography showed people the brutality of Balaclava, and the corpses of Rorke's Drift. As well photographs enabled people to appreciate the aesthetics of the sphinx and the pyramids without being there. It soon became evident that this form of photography based on authenticity, truth and reality had an intrinsic artistic merit to it that owed nothing to painting. Oliver Wendell Holmes described the value of the photograph as a form of artistic expression by saying 'the very things which an artist would leave out or render imperfectly, the photograph takes infinite care with and so renders the illusion perfect'.

It was almost inevitable that photography would find its artistic identity through photo-journalism even though the incentive behind this form of photography was the historical record and the newsworthy picture. The American civil war photography of Gardner, O'Sullivan, Brady and others, the photographic records of explorers and adventurers such as John Buckley Green,

SOCIETE FRANCAISE DE PHOTOGRAPHIE

Félix Nadar
Portrait of Hector Berlioz,
French composer, 1803–1869.
Collodion
1859

the Bisson brothers, Vandiveer Hayden and others, gave a view of life and death and of human civilization that had no counterpart in any previous art.

In the later part of the 19th century the influence of photographic realism began to alter the accepted view of artistic expression. Photographers were becoming more knowledgeable about the technology and the science of photography and this provided them with a new self-confidence and respect for the technology and the medium. Pictures began to be taken which had intrinsic merit and individuality as pictures rather than being a derived or incidental relationship to an event or a person. The first alternative statement to the 'pictorialist' school of photography came from photographers such as Peter Henry Emerson (1856–1936) who saw the camera as an instrument for recording the sophistication of natural-ness. Emerson used the camera to simulate the processes of vision and human perception and he produced photographs which emphasized the most important elements of the subject by placing distractions and

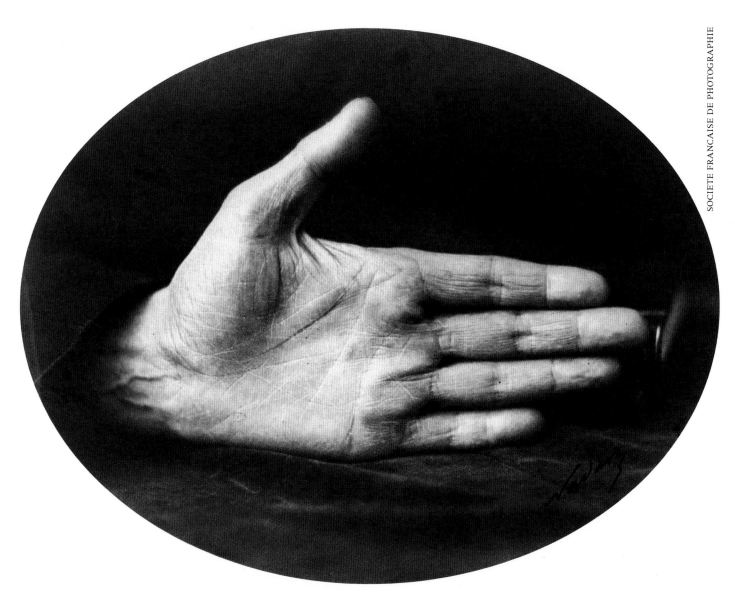

Félix Nadar
The hand of a banker; a chirographic study.
Collodion
1860

inconsequential aspects of the picture out of focus relative to the central image. By using this technique of selective focus, Emerson produced an eclectic view of the subject just as the human eye and brain focuses on certain elements of the visual field while subconsciously rejecting the rest. Emerson's influence on other photographers was great and his pronouncements carried considerable weight in contemporary photographic circles. However, after espousing the 'naturalistic' approach to photography, Emerson had a schizophrenic reaction to his earlier stand and in 1891 he renounced the existence of an association between 'naturalistic' photography and pictorial art.

The 'pictorialist' photographers continued to develop their artistic style and in Paris, the work of Robert Demachy and Puyo added strength to the movement. Demachy's photographs in particular, had a great popular appeal because of their sensitive, artistic qualities. While there was a degree of independence and self-confidence in Demachy's work, the particular romantic

SOCIETE FRANCAISE DE PHOTOGRAPHIE

Adrien
Nude with flowers and shawl.
Carbon shadowing technique with
Lumière autochrome plate
circa 1905

and aesthetic qualities of his pictures were difficult to disassociate from the impressionist art of the time. Many of Demachy's *avant-garde* photographs were published in the rather staid journal of the Royal Photographic Society of London and in the journal *Camera Work* run by the American photographer Stieglitz (1864–1946). Stieglitz had achieved an early notoriety through the success of his photographs in exhibitions and he organized a group of photographers in 1890 to form the Camera Club of New York. He concentrated on demonstrating the flexibility and adaptability of cameras and of photographic techniques in recording events outside the studio in all sorts of inappropriate conditions and circumstances. Another outstanding photographer of the time was

Hippolyte Bayard
Positive print on sodium
chloride treated paper.
The mill of Montmartre, from
original painting by Bayard.
Direct positive print
1843

SOCIETE FRANCAISE DE PHOTOGRAPHIE

IMAGES; ILLUSION AND REALITY

Edward Steichen (1879–1973) who shared Stieglitz's conviction of the artistic potentialities of photography. Together with colleagues such as Clarence White, Gertrude Käsebier and Steichen, Stieglitz founded the Photo-Secession Group in New York with the object of staging photographic exhibitions and improving artistic standards of photography in America. Similarly dedicated secession groups had also been formed in England (The Linked Ring Society), in France (The Photo Club de Paris) and in Germany and Austria. The journal of Photo-

Secession was 'Camera Work' and this presented, in quarterly editions, articles on photographic technique and art. The Group was instrumental in sponsoring impressionist and modern art exhibitions, lithographs

Hippolyte Bayard
Positive print on sodium
chloride treated paper.
The carpenter's house, from
original painting by Bayard.
Direct positive print
1843

SOCIETE FRANCAISE DE PHOTOGRAPHIE

and sculpture alongside contemporary photographic exhibitions at the famous 291 Gallery on Fifth Avenue. In 1910 the Group organized one of the most significant photographic exhibitions ever staged in America at the Albright-Knox Gallery in Buffalo. The exhibition was of enormous size and scope and caused a sensation at the time, doing much to popularize the public acceptance of photographic art. There was however, bound to be present within such a group of creative artists, differences of opinion about the aesthetic justification of the technical

and manipulative procedures used to produce non-photographic qualities in the negatives and prints. The purists wanted unretouched and unmanipulated photographs and a complete reliance on compositional and tonal effects to achieve their artistic ends. These conflicting aspirations were to lead eventually to the disintegration of the Group.

The claim that the unmanipulated image was the genuine form of photographic artistry was promoted by the works of many photographers in the early part of the

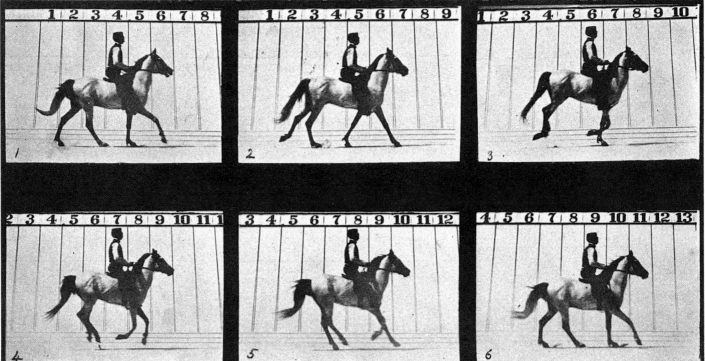

James E. Muybridge
The horse 'Mahomed'
photographed travelling at about
200 metres a minute.
(12 km/hr)

twentieth century. Weston, Adams, Van Dyke and others in America; Strand, first in America and then in Paris; Renger-Patzsch in Germany and Eugène Atget in France all sought perfection of photographic imagery in the forms and shapes of natural objects, avoiding any attempts at artistic interpretation or perception along the lines of painters.

The aesthetic possibilities of photography were now fully accredited as was its power to depict the beauty and ugliness of the natural world and of civilization. The camera was to be the instrument for the pictorial documentation of social change in terms of the joy, exhilaration, pleasure, pain, tragedy, desperation, hope and misery of human experience. The French photojournalist Gyula Halaz, recorded the activities of prostitutes, night club entertainers, drug addicts and other denizens of the Paris streets in his social commentary entitled 'Night People'. In another context, Josef Sudek (1886–1976) documented the administrative, commercial, business and social style of the city of Prague, while

Alfred Ehrmann
Jumping over a rope; an early example of action photography.
Collodion
1892

Brandt photographed the life of London during the depression and the second world war. The extraordinary feature of this 'social' photography is the seeming acceptance of the photographers themselves as elements of the cultures and subcultures being photographed. Because of this the photographic documentation seems not to compromise the privacy or the intimacy of what are quite public events.

While photography took the best part of 100 years to overcome its self-consciousness and obligations towards painting and other art forms, the implicit strength of photographic expression inevitably has exerted its own influence on both the visual and the plastic arts. Modern and abstract art has made use of photographic imaging to produce and interpret patterns of light without using the camera and the lens. These abstract photographic interpretations have some of the qualities of surrealist paintings. Làzlò Moholy-Nagy (1895–1946), the Hungarian abstract artist working in Berlin was one of the first to exploit the technical capabilities of photography

E. Fierlants
The royal palace in Brussels.
Collodion
1860

to produce visible images of invisible subjects and thus interpret the artistic and aesthetic qualities of illusions and unrealities. His book *Painting, Photography, Film,* published in 1925, dealt with these aspects of the visual perception of the invisible. The capacity to represent and interpret structures that are non-existent until they are given shape and form by photography was just one aspect of a completely new awareness by artists of the 1920's and 30's that the full scope of artistic definition could not be had simply through the use of classical art

materials and techniques. A range of media as diverse as precious stones, metals and garbage refuse as well as paint and film became legitimate materials for artistic expression. Collages and three dimensional pictures using objects glued to a background gave a novel expressive effect to paintings and, at the same time, foreshadowed what was to be the most stunning transition in artistic technique and medium since the masterpieces of the Lascaux caves were produced. The quest for further spatial and interpretive dimensions in the visual

Joseph Albert
Interior of the Crystal Palace in Munich.
Collodion
1865

Joseph Albert
The Crystal Palace during construction.
These large prints were taken using a Steinheil 90° 'Periscope' objective lens. Exposure time 1½ minutes.

arts produced the motion picture but the discovery of the optical basis of image formation and how the human eye and brain reconstruct this image, has given the photographer and the artist the ultimate photographic illusion — the hologram. The availability of a new approach to a third dimensional interpretation of ideas and perceptions and the certain addition of the fourth dimension of time to this medium will require a new analysis and interpretation of art, illusion and reality. So far holographic photography has taken only a few tentative steps into the art world of the future and the holograms being produced today are probably equivalent to the Calotypes of Fox Talbot and Hippolyte Bayard in terms of their technical evolution. Already there are the most startling artistic possibilities in colour holography using techniques which allow the illuminating light to be separated into its spectral colours to give a hologram which reveals the image in one or other of the colours of

Kock and Wilz
Panorama of Paris taken with a
device invented by the
photographers.
Collodion
1857

L. Godefroy
Quay and harbour, Saint
Nazaire. Panoramic view
composed from three prints 14 x
14 cm.

SOCIETE FRANCAISE DE PHOTOGRAPHIE

IMAGES; ILLUSION AND REALITY

the rainbow.

The science of optical wave-form analysis will certainly lead to the use of holograms to depict three dimensional forms of objects that interact with electromagnetic radiation beyond the visible spectrum. These illusions of non-existent shapes will enable both scientific and artistic interpretations and statements to be made about a world whose reality requires that it exists only as a part of our subjective thoughts and mental imagery. Science has expanded the artistic horizons of photography into the limitless universe of the galaxies, the microcosm of the cell and even to the world of the molecule and the atom. The extraordinary thing is that the photographic representation of shapes and forms at the level of these two incomprehensible abstractions has already demonstrated that the aesthetics of these disparate worlds will be a source of wonder and inspiration for the photographers and artists of the next 150 years.

SOCIETE FRANCAISE DE PHOTOGRAPHIE

SOCIETE FRANCAISE DE PHOTOGRAPHIE

Moessard
The machinery hall at the 1900 Exhibition. Photograph taken with a 'Moessard' panoramic device.
Panorama
1900

Alphonse Poitevin
The first photolithograph by Poitevin. The print is signed by the author.
Photolithograph
1855

Beyond this one can envisage the artistic and aesthetic analysis of all elements of energy and matter by photography and perhaps eventually a pictorial analysis of the beauty and symmetry of a mathematical formula, a physical equation or even a thought.

Adrien
The Adrien family on holiday.
Carbon shadowing technique with
Lumière autochrome plate
circa 1905

SOCIETE FRANCAISE DE PHOTOGRAPHIE

SOCIETE FRANCAISE DE PHOTOGRAPHIE

Adrien
Alpine climbers on a glacier.
Carbon shadowing technique with
Lumière autochrome plate
circa 1905

Paul Delondre
A large oak in the Bois de
Boulogne — positive Print.
Calotype — negative and positive
1859

Victor Régnault
The banks of the Seine near
Meudon.
*Reproduction by Claudine Sudre
from original negative*
1850

J.N. Nièpce
Cardinal d'Amboise.
Print taken from a photo
engraving done by the engraver
Lemaitre.
Heliographic Print
1827

SOCIETE FRANCAISE DE PHOTOGRAPHIE

SOCIETE FRANCAISE DE PHOTOGRAPHIE

J.N. Nièpce
The Holy Family.
Heliographic Plate
1827

L.D. Blanquart-Evrard
The oriental colossus of Speos.
Photographs by J.B. Green taken
from a book edited by
Blanquart-Evrard.
Calotypes
1854

SOCIETE FRANCAISE DE PHOTOGRAPHIE

Paul Pretsch
'Don Quixote' in his dressing
room. Photograph by William
Price — print from a
photogalvanographic plate by
Pretsch.
Photogalvanograph
date unknown

IMAGES; ILLUSION AND REALITY

SOCIETE FRANCAISE DE PHOTOGRAPHIE

SOCIETE FRANCAISE DE PHOTOGRAPHIE

Alphonse Poitevin
Memoirs of a madman.
Photolithograph
1856

C. Nègre
Portrait of Theophile Gautier,
French writer 1811–1872.
Heliographic print
1857

Franck de Villecholle
Portrait of two young girls.
Collodion
1868

SOCIETE FRANCAISE DE PHOTOGRAPHIE

SOCIETE FRANCAISE DE PHOTOGRAPHIE

Alphonse Poitevin
Picture of a woman.
Photolithograph
1855

SOCIETE FRANCAISE DE PHOTOGRAPHIE

Auguste Bertsch and Camille Arnaud
Portrait of an actor.
Collodion
1857

IMAGES; ILLUSION AND REALITY

SOCIETE FRANCAISE DE PHOTOGRAPHIE

Auguste Bertsch and Camille Arnaud
Portrait of Adelaide Ristori the Italian Tragedienne 1821–1906.
Collodion
1857

Oscar-Gustave Rejlander
A study of hands.
Collodion
1857

SOCIETE FRANCAISE DE PHOTOGRAPHIE

IMAGES; ILLUSION AND REALITY

Gustave Le Gray
Portrait of Comte Nieuwerkerke.
Collodion
1859

Gustave Le Gray
Portrait of a young girl.
Collodion
1857

Félix Nadar
Portrait of Sarah Bernhardt,
French actress 1844–1923.
Eastman paper print
undated

Félix Nadar
Portrait of Victor Hugo, French
writer, 1802–1885.
Collodion
1885

SOCIETE FRANCAISE DE PHOTOGRAPHIE

Félix Nadar
Portrait of the painter and
lithographic artist Honoré
Daumier 1808–1879.
Collodion
1859

IMAGES; ILLUSION AND REALITY

Félix Nadar
Portrait of Eugène Pelletan,
French socialist politician,
1813–1885.
Collodion
1859

SOCIETE FRANCAISE DE PHOTOGRAPHIE

Félix Nadar
Portrait of the son of Musard,
composer of popular songs and
the proprietor of the celebrated
ballroom *Le bal Mabille*.
Collodion
1859

Félix Nadar
Portrait of Palazzi.
Collodion
1859

IMAGES; ILLUSION AND REALITY

Paul Nadar
Group portrait of Russian school
girls.
Gelatin bromide
circa 1900

P. Perier
Wild game.
Collodion
1850

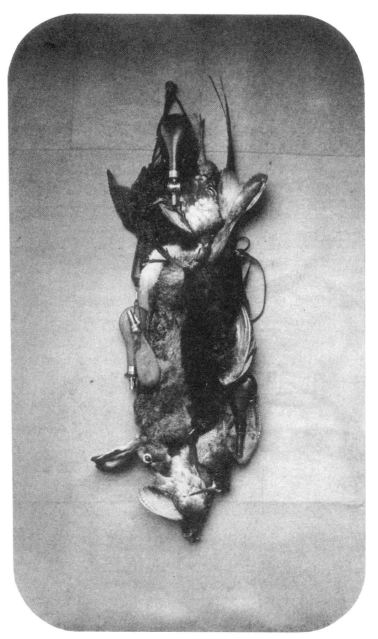

SOCIETE FRANCAISE DE PHOTOGRAPHIE

Adolphe Bilordeaux
Objets d' Art.
Albumin Collodion negative-positive
coated with gold
1857

E. Chauvigné
Floral arrangements.
Photoglyptic process
1876

E. Chauvigné
Floral arrangements.
Photoglyptic process
1876

SOCIETE FRANCAISE DE PHOTOGRAPHIE

SOCIETE FRANCAISE DE PHOTOGRAPHIE

Paul Nadar
Two prints: An interview with
Chevreul on his 101st birthday.
Chevreul — French Chemist
1786–1889.
Gelatin-silver bromide
1887

SOCIÉTÉ FRANCAISE DE PHOTOGRAPHIE

Photographer unknown
Modern woman. Photograph
taken in artificial light as a send
up of Marie Curie.
Gelatin-silver bromide
date unknown

Nadar Jeune;
Adrien Tournachon
The piper.
Collodion
1857

Robert Demachy
Young girl.
Bichromate gum arabic print
circa 1900

SOCIETE FRANCAISE DE PHOTOGRAPHIE

Robert Demachy
Portrait of a young girl.
Oil transfer
circa 1900

SOCIETE FRANCAISE DE PHOTOGRAPHIE

SOCIETE FRANCAISE DE PHOTOGRAPHIE

Robert Demachy
Portrait of a woman.
Oil transfer process
circa 1900

Robert Demachy
Portrait of a woman.
Oil transfer process
circa 1900

Robert Demachy
The reader.
Transfer proess
circa 1900

Robert Demachy
Profile of a woman.
Bichromate gum arabic print
circa 1900

Robert Demachy
Nudes amongst nature.
Oil transfer process
circa 1900

SOCIETE FRANCAISE DE PHOTOGRAPHIE

Robert Demachy
Woman on the beach.
Transfer process
circa 1900

SOCIETE FRANCAISE DE PHOTOGRAPHIE

C. Puyo
Woman in oriental dress.
Artigue paper
1895

C. Puyo
Repose. Woman reclining on a
sofa.
Artigue paper
1895

SOCIETE FRANCAISE DE PHOTOGRAPHIE

C. Puyo
Beside the water.
Carbon
undated

C. Puyo
Profile, study in lighting.
Carbon
undated

C. **Puyo**
Veil effect.
Carbon
undated

SOCIETE FRANCAISE DE PHOTOGRAPHIE

Robert Demachy
Portrait of Mademoiselle P.
Oil transfer process
circa 1900

SOCIETE FRANCAISE DE PHOTOGRAPHIE

C. Puyo
The nude — a project for a book
Bichromate gum arabic print
1905

SOCIETE FRANCAISE DE PHOTOGRAPHIE

SOCIETE FRANCAISE DE PHOTOGRAPHIE

C. Puyo
Portrait of a woman.
Transfer process in 3 colours
1905

C. Puyo
Woman with a hat.
Bichromate gum arabic print
1905

C. Puyo
Woman with a parasol.
Carbon
undated

Robert Demachy
Mother & child.
Orange bichromate
circa 1900

Robert Demachy
Madeleine. Profile of a young girl.
Oil transfer process
circa 1900

IMAGES; ILLUSION AND REALITY

C. Puyo
A woman.
Bichromate gum arabic print
undated

Robert Demachy
Nude — (tinted).
Bichromate gum arabic print
circa 1900

Robert Demachy
Nude in profile.
Oil transfer process
circa 1900

C. Puyo
Water lilies.
Artigue paper
undated

C. Puyo
Nude amongst nature.
Artigue paper
undated

SOCIETE FRANCAISE DE PHOTOGRAPHIE

SOCIETE FRANCAISE DE PHOTOGRAPHIE

Léon Gimpel
Education fair at the Galérie des
Machines. Free distribution of
stamped illustrated post-cards.
*Black and white print from original
negative*
June 1904

SOCIETE FRANCAISE DE PHOTOGRAPHIE

Léon Gimpel
At the fairground — The
Canadian slide — A difficult
ascent.
*Black and white print from original
negative*
July 1905

SOCIETE FRANCAISE DE PHOTOGRAPHIE

Léon Gimpel
At the fairground. The Canadian
slide.
*Black and white print from original
negative*
July 1905

Peter Henry Emerson
A pastoral interlude. Print taken
from the book *Pictures of East-
Anglican life.*
Photomechanical process
1888

C. Puyo
Silhouette in a glade.
Carbon
circa 1900

Léon Gimpel
The Aeronautical Salon in the
esplanade of the Invalides.
Autochrome reproduction

IMAGES; ILLUSION AND REALITY

SOCIETE FRANCAISE DE PHOTOGRAPHIE

Léon Gimpel
1st International Exposition on
aerial navigation.
Autochrome reproduction
1904

Léon Gimpel
The Fanfare.
Autochrome reproduction
1904

SOCIETE FRANCAISE DE PHOTOGRAPHIE

Holography and holographic art

The light that never was on sea of land,
The consecration, and the poets dream
WILLIAM WORDSWORTH

Holography is a technique by which a three dimensional image can be recorded on a two dimensional piece of film. A Hungarian physicist, Dennis Gabor, originally developed the holographic process in 1947 as a means of improving the resolution of images produced by transmission electronmicroscopy. Even though Gabor's objective was not achieved, holography has opened up a whole new dimension to scientists and artists that had previously been inaccessible to exploration or exploitation. Already holograms are being produced for a startling range of applications; for new types of optical elements, for security logos on credit cards, for information storage and transmission, for microscopic studies and for 3-dimensional displays.

The essence of the holographic process is that it records not just the reflected light which has illuminated an object, but an interference pattern created by two different light sources — a combination of unadulterated, coherent light direct from a laser source and reflected, scattered light from an object illuminated by that same laser. Portrayal of an illusory object in three dimensions is achieved by reilluminating the photographic plate (the captured interference pattern) reproducing exactly the light waves originally incident upon it.

Because of the difficulty of producing a really coherent light source of adequate intensity, holography made little progress initially, even though the theoretical and practical potentialities of the procedure were obvious. Like many scientific developments, another discovery was needed to allow the theoretical possibilities of holography to be translated into practical results. This was the discovery of light amplification by stimulated emission of radiation — the 'laser'. The theoretical basis for the laser was developed from work done by Einstein in 1917 and by Kastler in 1949 though it was Schawlow and Townes in 1958, who demonstrated the feasibility of light amplification by stimulated emission. The first functioning laser was constructed in 1960 by Maiman.

Two types of lasers are used for holography; lasers which emit a monochromatic beam of light continuously and pulsed lasers which emit flashes of intense monochromatic light with a duration of a fraction of a millionth of a second. Pulsed-laser holography makes the production of portraits of living subjects possible and has scientific and technical applications in recording rapid chemical reactions, high speed air flow patterns and the images of liquid droplets and emulsions. Transient deformations in structures can be recorded by comparing pulsed holograms of the same subject taken before and while it is stressed. Any deformation in the subject shows up as an interference pattern formed by the two sets of light waves and these differences can be measured with an accuracy better than a ten-thousandth of a millimetre.

Holographic images have been recorded on a variety of light sensitive materials. The most common are, of course, high resolution photographic materials. An alternative is the use of plates or film coated with dichromated gelatin which hardens locally on exposure to light, or plastic monomers susceptible to photopolymerization. For some technical applications, it is convenient to record holograms on a photothermoplastic which can be erased and reused.

The making of a hologram

All changed, changed utterly,
A terrible beauty is born.
W.B. YEATS

The actual procedure for making a hologram involves passing a laser beam through a splitting device to divide it into two beams; one beam is directed at the subject while the other, the reference beam, is directed onto a photographic plate. The beam striking the subject is scattered by the subject's features onto the photographic plate while the reference beam is directed to the plate by way of a reflecting mirror. As a consequence each tiny segment of the plate is illuminated by some light from both beams. The interference pattern on the plate is created by the reinforcement of the light intensity in areas of the plate where the waves from the two beams are in phase and by the reduction in light intensity where the waves are out of phase and cancel one another. The interference pattern is unique for the subject and for its position in relation to the photographic plate. The photographic plate when developed becomes a hologram. The interference pattern although unrecognizable in terms of the subject contains all the optical information necessary

IMAGES; ILLUSION AND REALITY

to reconstruct a three dimensional image of the subject. This information is registered on the photographic plate as densely arranged patterns of interference fringes which appear as minute black and white lines. The image is reconstructed from the hologram by directing a reference beam onto it in the appropriate geometry. As this beam strikes the plate the interference fringes diffract the light to produce a positive image of the original subject. Looking back through the plate the viewer sees the image of the object in the position it occupied when it was illuminated by the primary laser beam. Different perspectives of the object can be seen depending on the position of the viewer.

To record a hologram with a continuous wave laser, the subject must be immobile and absolutely stable. Any movement of the subject, by even a fraction of the wavelength of the laser light, destroys the holographic image. However, holograms can be made with a pulsed laser without concern for subject stability, because the period of exposure is so short that movement becomes irrelevant.

Paula Dawson
The Eidola Suite
Paula Dawson on Set of 1st
Hologram.
Photograph by Terence Bogue.

IMAGES; ILLUSION AND REALITY

The essence of the holographic process is that it records not just the reflected light which has illuminated an object, but an interference pattern created by two different light sources — a combination of unadulterated, coherent light direct from a laser source and reflected, scattered light from an object illuminated by that same laser. Portrayal of an illusory object in three dimensions is achieved by reilluminating the photographic plate (the captured interference pattern) reproducing exactly the light waves originally incident upon it.

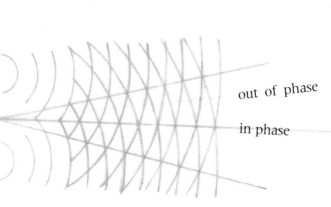

out of phase

in phase

Simulation of an interference pattern created by two point-sources of light. Where the crests of each wave are in synchrony (solid line) they amplify one another (increased light intensity), but where the crests of two waves are in asynchrony (dotted line) they cancel one another (decreased light intensity).

photographic plate

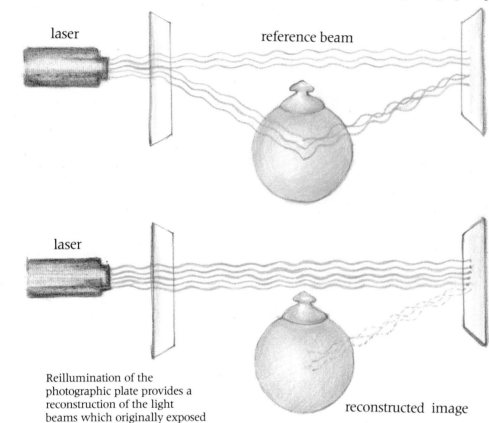

laser

reference beam

Apparatus used to make a holographic image of a vase. Note that a mirror or prism will deflect a portion of the laser light directly towards the photographic plate, while the rest is used to illuminate the object.

laser

Reillumination of the photographic plate provides a reconstruction of the light beams which originally exposed

reconstructed image

the film, thus the apparent position of the object is actually behind the surface of the film.

Left

Right

ADRIAN YOUNG

Stereo photographs of Paula Dawson and part of 'The Eidola Suite' of holograms.

White light holograms

The classical method of making a hologram imposes certain inconvenient restrictions on its subsequent display. Firstly, the hologram requires a bright monochromatic light source such as a laser for illumination. Secondly, the image is in a single colour, derived from the laser light source.

The inconvenience of having to use a laser or some other source of monochromatic light to illuminate the hologram can be overcome in two ways. One way is to make what is termed a reflection hologram. In making a reflection hologram the reference beam is arranged so as to illuminate the photographic plate from behind. When the plate is developed and illuminated from in front with white light, the interference patterns recorded within the thickness of the emulsion layer recreate a monochromatic image of the subject.

Another method is to make a secondary hologram which can then be viewed with transmitted white light. To do this a primary hologram is first constructed in the

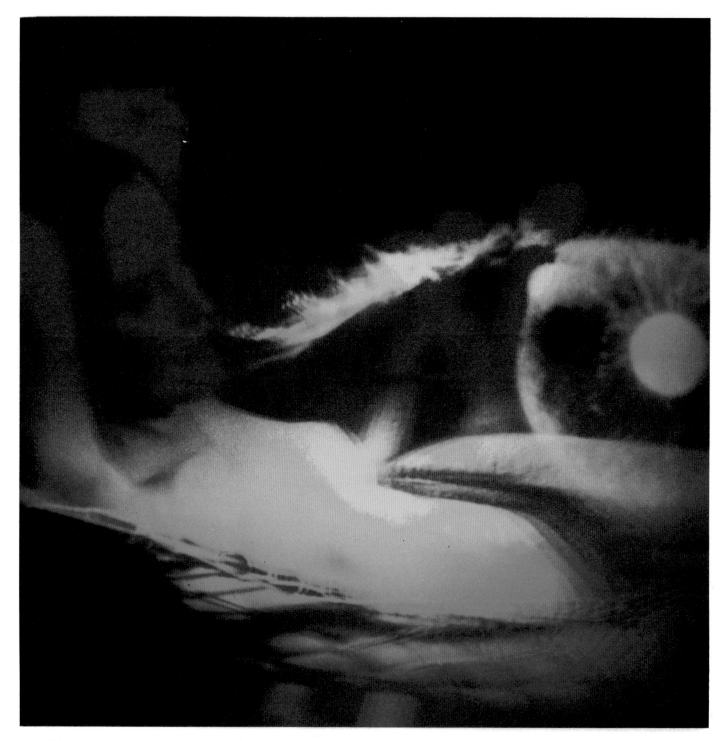

Danielle's dream.
Hologram by Alexander.

usual way and illuminated so as to produce an undistorted real image (an image than can be photographed) of the subject; this image then becomes the subject for a secondary hologram. The view of the primary hologram is restricted by a horizontal slit during the making of the secondary hologram. The second hologram consists of the interference patterns created by the diffracted beam from the first hologram interacting with a new reference beam. The second hologram when reconstructed with a beam of monochromatic light produces, in addition to

region of overlap of these spectra corresponds to the laser wavelengths from which the original separation holograms were made. The hologram when viewed from this region of overlap reveals a full colour, three dimensional image of the subject.

Holographic Stereograms
A further development in holographic technique has led to the production of what are termed 'holographic stereograms'. These holograms can also be produced

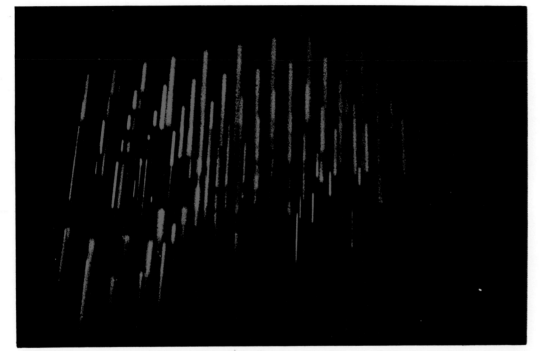

Seventh movement.
Hologram by Alexander.

an image of the original subject, an image of the slit. The viewer can only see the subject, by positioning his line of sight within the projected image of the slit. Vertical parallax is lost, but the image can be seen from various vantages in the horizontal plane and there is no loss in depth perception. The brightness of the image is enormously enhanced because all the light goes to form the image within the slit. With white light the image changes colour as the observer moves his line of sight up and down, but at all times he sees a sharp image in a single colour. This type of hologram is commonly known as a 'rainbow' hologram.

The technique has been extended to produce full-colour images by Hariharan and his colleagues of CSIRO. To do this three primary holograms of the subject have to be produced with red, green and blue lasers. Each colour separation hologram is illuminated through a narrow slit by the same laser which produced it, to give the real images for a multiply exposed, secondary hologram. When this hologram is illuminated with white light, three superimposed images of the subject appear in the viewing space along with three images of the slit which are spread in the vertical plane to form three spectra. The

with live subjects, because not only is immobility unimportant for the production of the hologram, but deliberate movement by the subject can be reproduced in the image. In the first part of the procedure the subject is placed on a rotating stage in front of a movie camera which records a series of pictures from a number of different angles. Alternatively, the camera can be traversed across the front of the subject. The film is then developed and the pictures are projected sequentially onto a ground glass screen with a special projector, rather like a movie projector except that its light source is a laser beam. A series of abutting vertical strip holograms of the projected images is registered on a long film which is advanced between exposures. This master hologram is then used to make a secondary transmission hologram which can be viewed with white light. The holographic stereogram presents slightly different images to each eye of the observer, which are fused stereoscopically to give a three-dimensional image.

Cinematic holography
Three-dimensional movies have a history that extends from the work of William Friese-Green in the 1890's.

IMAGES; ILLUSION AND REALITY

Various methods have been used to amalgamate the images presented to the two eyes so as to give a stereoscopic effect. These methods include the use of periscopes, prisms, rotating shutters and other devices that are inconvenient for the viewer while watching motion pictures. Techniques using red and green images viewed through appropriate filtered spectacles, one for each eye, or using polarized light have so far failed to gain any acceptance. This was also the case with a technique devised by the Russian scientist Ivanov in 1941 for viewing 3-D films without spectacles by projecting the film on a screen which had a grid of fine copper wires placed in such a way on it that parallax prevented the left eye from seeing the right image and vice versa.

In 1978 the Russian motion picture research association NIKFI demonstrated a holographic movie produced by a camera which operated with a pulsed ruby laser to produce the primary illumination and secondary reference beams. The holograms were recorded on film which ran at a speed of 1 metre per second and the

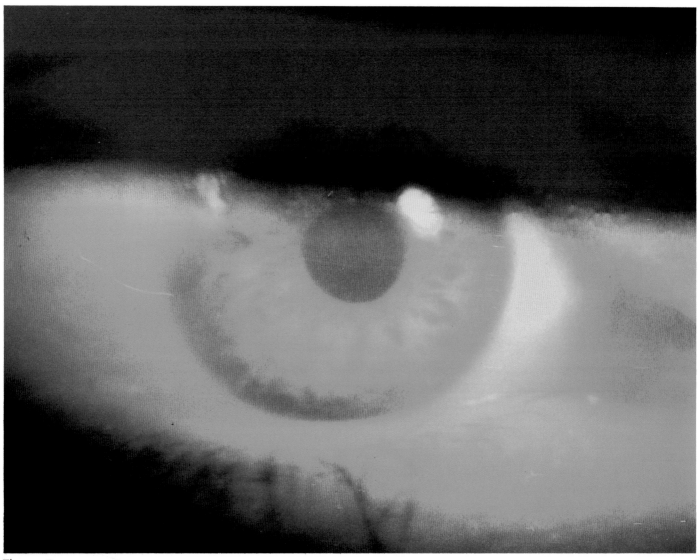

The eye, One.
Hologram by Alexander.

holographic image was projected onto a special screen, itself produced holographically.

In 1985 scientists at the Institut St Louis directed by Smigielski were awarded the Grand Prix International du Futur for their work on cinematic holography. The Institut presented two holographic films at the Salon International des Techniques et Energies du Futur (SITEF 85) which demonstrated the artistic and industrial potentialities of holographic movies. The first film 'Christiane et les Holobulles' showed a young woman blowing bubbles to the audience. The second film 'Holoparleur' demonstrated the holographic deformation of the membrane of a loud speaker as it vibrated to produce particular sounds. This 3-D movie technique has the potential for studying physical phenomena such as stress deformations in material in four dimensions for the first time. Many other applications for this technique can be predicted in the near future.

Holographic Art

The scientific and technical development of the laser and the development of theories in optical physics which led to the invention and perfection of holography provide a marvellous example of the influence of science and scientific thought on art. The artistic potential of holography was recognized almost from the outset of its discovery and was soon seen as a technique which allowed the creation of works of art in which all the features of painting, sculpture and photography could be combined in a single medium. The fugacious and intangible quality of the holographic image, changing with the viewer's perspective and vantage point, suspended in space and encompassing its own 3 dimensional void resembles in many respects, the conceptual image of the subject within the mind of the artist. The executed hologram is, in a sense, the public projection of the artist's private thoughts.

Holography is the integration of sculptural form with photography and it uses light rather than stone, bronze or wood as the medium with which to fashion a three dimensional image in space. It is the spatial dimension that is unique to holography for it has special characteristics and rules of behaviour that can be understood and exploited to transport artistic interpretations into another world of illusion. These interpretations have a sensuality, mood, colour and movement that cannot exist in a conventional painting, photograph or sculpture. The reason for this lies in the strength and authenticity of the hologram which compels the mind of the viewer to provide any missing elements in the image to complete the illusion. This is done almost instantaneously when holograms of familiar subjects are being viewed but quite severe perceptive and interpretive challenges confront the mind of the viewer when presented with holograms of abstract subjects and unfamiliar objects which have no mental reference points from which to verify the image.

New giant multicolour white-light and laser holograms have recently been produced as the result of collaboration between the creative minds of artists and scientists. Alexander has produced for the first time, major holograms and holographic sculptures up to 2 metres wide and 1 metre high portraying the full length human figure in three dimensions. Paula Dawson's holograms of room interiors, landscapes, trees and houses develop the three dimensional illusion in a way never attempted before.

These holograms are technically awesome and they represent transitional forms of holographic expression as significant as the Daguerreotype and the Calotype were in the evolution of photography. Artistically they portray a development in visual imagery whose impact on the viewer is stunning. They are figurative works and sculptured performances in which spatial and temporal dimensions determine the viewer's appreciation of the artistic image. The images have even greater fidelity than those of conventional photographs but the illusion floats in space, it moves with the viewer and is not there when the viewer reaches out to touch it. For the first time holographic space is exploited as a dimension in which the essential unreality of the interpreted image is projected as a telephotopathic extension of the artist's mental imagery. The viewer of these remarkable artistic creations has no difficulty in associating the image with both the illusion and its reality.

The remarkable technical and artistic achievements in holography need to be appreciated in the context of a discovery that is only 30 years old. The present stage of development of holography is probably comparable to the development of photography around 1850. There is no doubt that given a similar period of evolution to the photographic process, the contributions of holography in science, industry and art will be every bit as overwhelming. However, at present there are many practical problems which prevent the theoretical realization of the process from being translated into a perfect pictorial result.

Holography presents a challenge to the contemporary creative artist not only because of the newness and unfamiliarity of the process but also because of the complexities of the still unresolved physical and optical problems relating to the process, the technical difficulties associated with the medium and the largely unexplored status of the technology for artistic expression. It is the most perfect example of a process in which collaboration between the scientific mind and the artistic temperament offers unrivalled opportunities for artistic expression and statement. Further developments of holography combined with computer graphics will certainly allow artists to develop images of realities and illusions constructed from theories and hypotheses. At this point there can be no distinction between art and science.

Photomicroscopy and
the universe of the living cell

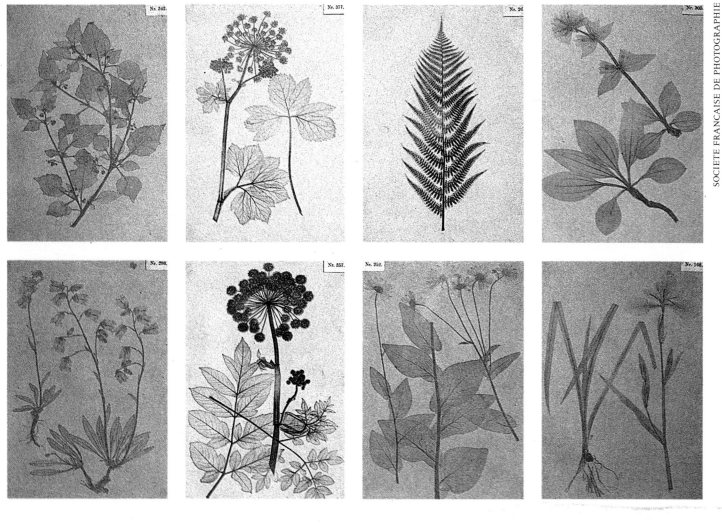

SOCIETE FRANCAISE DE PHOTOGRAPHIE

Photographer unknown
Photographic reproductions
from the physiolypia plant
collection. Set of eight prints.
Calotype
1855

IMAGES; ILLUSION AND REALITY

*While ruder heads stand amazed
at these prodigious pieces of nature,
as Elephants, Dromedaries and
Camels; these I confesse, are the
Colossus and majestick pieces of
her hand; but in these narrow Engines
there is more curious Mathematicks, and the
civility of these little Citizens, more
nearly sets forth the wisdome of their Maker.*

THOMAS BROWNE 1642

The development of the optical microscope and polished glass magnifying lenses led to the discovery of the world of microbes and of plant and animal cells. Beyond this, scientific developments in measurement and observation have revealed details of the internal structure of the cell down to the level of the molecular organization of life itself. The first description of plant cells was given by Robert Hooke in 1665 and of animal cells by Antoine Van Leeuwenhoek in 1673. Leeuwenhoek was a draper, chamberlain and

SOCIETE FRANCAISE DE PHOTOGRAPHIE

William Fox Talbot
Leaves and flowers.
Original Calotype
1841

wine gauger from the Dutch town of Delft. He had no formal training in physics, mathematics or optics but he had a surveyor's ticket and a special talent for constructing magnifying lenses of very high quality which he used in his studies of the formed elements of the blood, serum, semen and other body fluids and of bacteria, protozoa, and other microscopic *animalcules* for the first time.

Van Leeuwenhoek's perception of these objects was formed without the benefit of any previous experience of them. He interpreted the *animalcules* to be preformed microscopic extrapolations of larger entities which arose by spontaneous generation. He examined his own spermatozoa under the microscope 'obtained from the overplus of marital intercourse without committing any sin' and not being able to photograph what he saw, he drew pictures and described these tadpole-like cells. Leeuwenhoek saw the movements of the tail of the sperm and described within the tail, vessels, muscles and nerves which he could not possibly have seen.

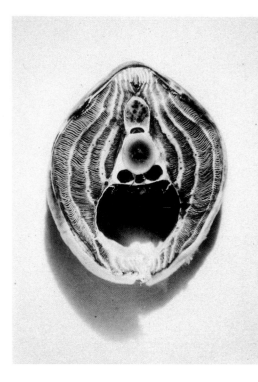

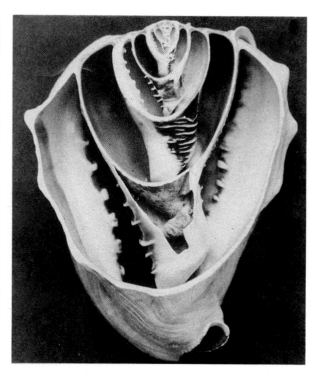

A.L. Donnadieu
The mouth of a lamprey
photographed under water with
the *Physiographe universel.*
Collodion
1883

Louis Rousseau
Shell shaped like a helmet.
Photograph taken at the
Museum of Natural History.
Collodion
1857

Auguste Bertsch
Silica crystals in polarised light.
Prints presented to the
Academie des Sciences, 10th
August 1857.
Collodion
1857

'In spite of their marvellous subtlety, these tails must have as many joints as the tails of the largest animal since they can move them with such splendid agility. Each of these joints must have muscles, nerves, arteries and veins of their own and there must be circulating fluids which provide them with nourishment, force and movements. The mind is lost in considering a smallness which is beyond our comprehension and yet our reason tells us that these things certainly exist.'

Leeuwenhoek argued that the anatomical features of the whole animal were present in its sperm cells in a miniaturized form. Plantade, around 1700, went further than Leeuwenhoek in developing the theory of preformation by demonstrating with line drawings of human sperm, legions of *animalculi* in human form. These *homunculi* were illustrated as microscopic abstractions of mannequins with arms, legs and face folded within the head of the sperm, like an unborn child in the uterus. Leeuwenhoek, Plantade and many of their contem-

L. Ducos du Hauron
Leaves and petals of flowers.
Carbon trichrome contact print
1869

Delarche
Leaves and flowers.
Colour photograph
1875

poraries and successors in microscopy, who were committed from the outset to a preformation theory of living things, could hardly do other than see what they were already convinced in their minds would be there.

The reality of the visual image of the cell had no meaning for Leeuwenhoek or Plantade so they created an appropriate illusion to explain what they could not see. One only has to think of Leeunwenhoek's emotions at seeing for the first time a microscopic universe that no one else had ever seen before, to realize that he had no

alternative but to represent what he saw to himself and to others as an abstraction of reality. After all, it has been man's habit since the beginning of time to create an intellectual framework to contain and give structure to things he could not explain. At this time there was no possibility of recording the microscopic images of cells by photography to establish their true morphology; this allowed artistic licence and interpretation to intrude into the evaluation of what was seen. Leeuwenhoek saw what he believed he saw because of a perception of these

Head and proboscis of the mosquito *Aedes silvestris*.

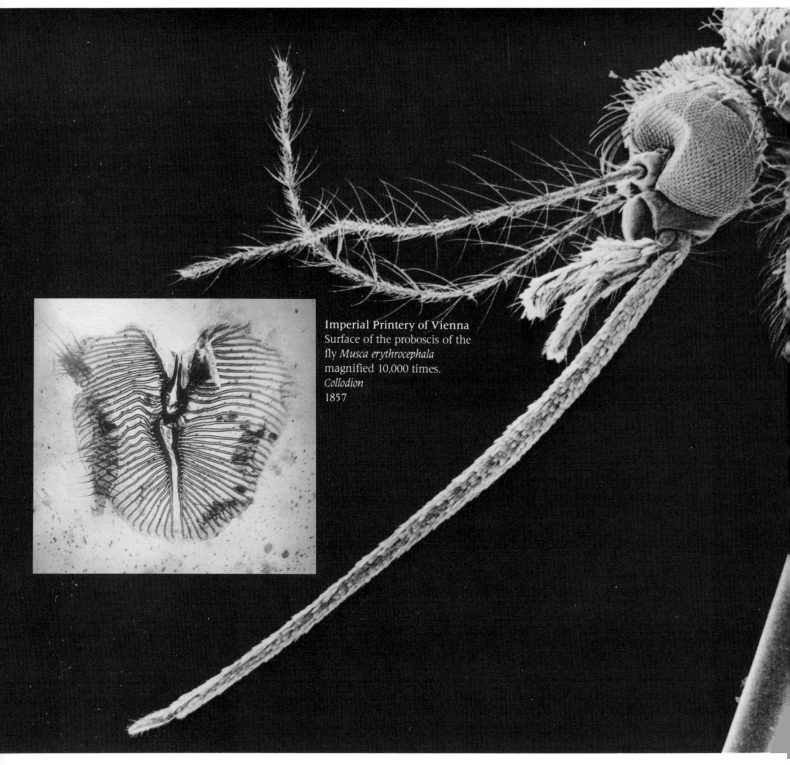

Imperial Printery of Vienna
Surface of the proboscis of the
fly *Musca erythrocephala*
magnified 10,000 times.
Collodion
1857

Scanning electronmicrograph, courtesy of C.S.I.R.O. Division of Entomology.

images developed within his brain. Much later successive generations of microscopists studied the form and structure of cells and tissues by embalming them and examining their corpses stained with dyes which show up the different parts of the cell. The pathologist looks at these brightly coloured replicas stained with haematoxylin and eosin and interprets their living status from the artefactual unreality of the image. Consciously he accepts the illusion even though he knows that real cells are not coloured red and blue.

The cell
The basic structural unit of an organism is the cell. While some organisms consist of one single cell most are made up of societies of cells associated in peculiar structural relationships with one another to form particular organs with particular functions. The activities of a cell depend on the organization of its molecular constitution. The arrangements of the ribonucleic acids, proteins, lipids and sugars in the cell into various organelles and structures, determines that the metabolic activities of the cell

The moth *Azaleodes fuscipes* showing microtrichia on one segment and scales on the adjacent segment.

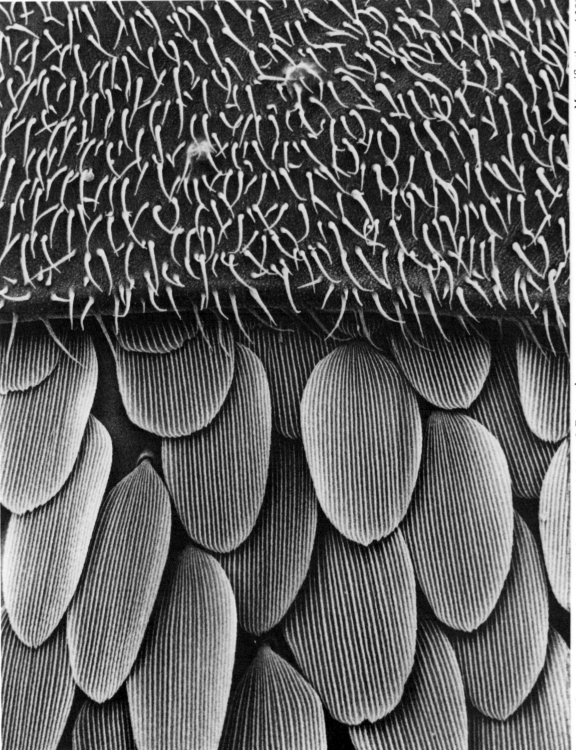

Magnification x 4,300

Scanning electronmicrograph, courtesy of C.S.I.R.O. Division of Entomology.

are spatially segregated. The phase boundary that enables the cell to exist as an independent living entity is its plasma membrane, the boundary between the internal and the external environment. This membrane has a unit structure of protein and glycolipid which confers on it a very high electrical resistance and a selective permeability. The principal organelles within the cell are the mitochondria involved in energy metabolism, the ribosomes concerned with protein synthesis and structural elements such as microtubules and microfibrils concerned with sustaining cell shape and allowing movement and mobility.

The genetic information which determines the form and function of a cell and finally the form and function of the organ and the organism, is contained within the nucleus in the form of chromatin or DNA. Communication between the nucleus and the cytoplasm takes place across the nuclear membrane, instructions passing mutually between the two compartments.

While a single cell is a biological entity of itself, multi-

cellular organisms require that individual cells communicate and associate with other cells to regulate the metabolism and function of the organism as a whole. Although every cell in a multicellular organism has the same genetic constitution, there are many morphologically and functionally different cells whose life-histories are determined by the particular portion of their genomes that is being expressed. Genetically a skin cell is not different from a liver cell or blood cell; it is just that during differentation certain of the potential capabilities of certain cell lines are suppressed while certain others are given expression to allow particular functions to develop.

Technical developments in microscopy

The structural and functional elements that comprise a cell and decide its life-history have been revealed by the microscope and recorded by photography. At first the earliest simple lens microscopes had magnifying capabilities of no more than a few diameters. Technical

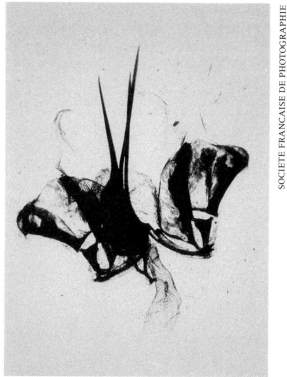

Auguste Bertsch
Photomicrograph. The antennae
of a fly.
Collodion
1857

Auguste Bertsch
Photomicrograph. Bee sting and
venom sac.
Collodion
1857

refinements in lens construction in the 17th century led to the production of optically ground lenses of sufficient quality and magnifying power to reveal the cellular structure of plant and animal tissues. These early lenses were developed empirically without any knowledge of the optical principles of dispersion, refraction or chromatic aberration. In 1830 Joseph Lister published a theoretical analysis and design for the construction of achromatic lenses free of aberrations and distortions due to curvature. The concept of expressing the resolving capability of a lens in terms of its aperture was developed by Ernst Abbe, a German physicist, in the late eighteen hundreds and his work led to the commercial development of optically corrected, distortion-free lenses.

For some time microscopists had realized that the resolving power of a microscope lens was related in some way to the angle of the cone of light entering the objective lens. Abbe demonstrated that the resolving power of a lens was proportional to the sine of the angle of aperture. This relationship was termed by Abbe the

Sting of the honeybee *Apis mellifera.*
magnification x 30

Scanning electronmicrograph, courtesy of C.S.I.R.O. Division of Entomology.

numerical aperture. Abbe also showed that when oil, water or some other medium was interposed between the objective lens and the specimen, the numerical aperture was increased by an amount related to the refractive index of the medium. The numerical aperture defines both the resolving power and the light-gathering capacity of a lens. The higher the numerical aperture of a lens the greater its resolution at any given wavelength of light.

Once the physical and mathematical calculations underlying the design and construction of microscope lenses were understood, compound microscopes were designed in which the objective lens was coupled with an eye-piece lens mounted within a tube so that the two could be moved relative to the object to bring the magnified image into focus. The principle of the compound microscope depends on the remagnification by the ocular lens of the magnified image produced by the objective lens. Both objective and ocular lenses can be removed and substituted by other lenses of different

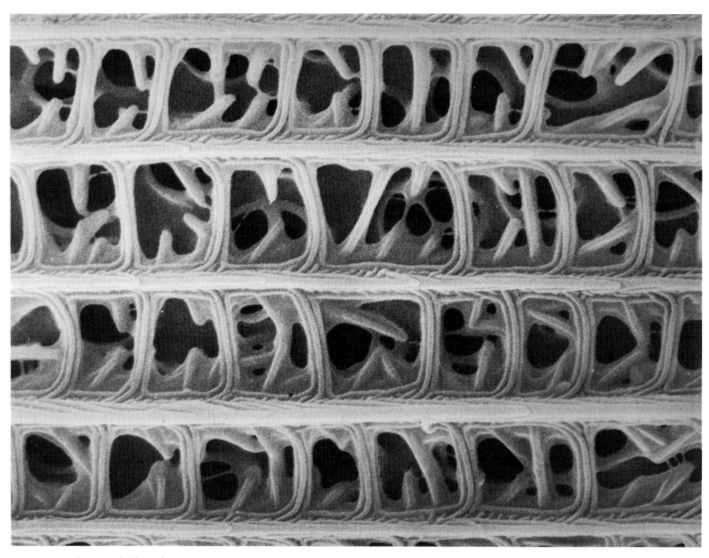

Wing scale of a Hepialoid moth,
Palaeores scholastica.
Magnification x 15,000

Scanning electronmicrograph,
courtesy of C.S.I.R.O. Division of
Entomology.

IMAGES; ILLUSION AND REALITY

apertures, focal lengths and resolving powers to produce a range of magnifications from 10 to as high as 2000 diameters for the transmitted light microscope.

The high magnifying capabilities of the compound microscope present problems of illumination, as the brightness of an image element is inversely proportional to the square of the magnification. It is crucial to have sufficient light entering through the objective lense to produce an image of adequate brightness. Combinations of condensers and lenses can be attached to the micro-scope below the specimen stage to concentrate light onto the subject.

The objective lens of a compound microscope pro-duces a magnified real image at a distance behind its focal plane lying within the tube of the microscope. The capability of a lens to magnify objects and at the same time to reveal fine detail, is a function of the optical qualities and design of the lens. Objective lenses are con-structed with different focal lengths varying from 75mm for low power lenses down to 2mm for the highest

The head of a *Strepsipteran,* an order of parasitic insects.
Magnification x 280

Scanning electronmicrograph, courtesy of C.S.I.R.O. Division of Entomology.

IMAGES; ILLUSION AND REALITY

power. Lenses of high quality are corrected for chromatic and spherical aberration, astigmatism, distortion and curvature of field of view. These characteristics, if left uncorrected, give a distorted and misleading magnified image to the observer's eye. For example uncorrected spherical abberration produces an unclear, hazy, ill-defined image while chromatic aberration leads to the appearance of coloured interference rings around the edges of the image. Astigmatism blurs the borders of the subject image when viewed in different focal planes.

An important aspect of microscopy is the arrangement of the illuminating light source to provide a focused beam of light of a numerical aperture that matches the objective lens. This is achieved through the use of a light condenser which has a double or triple lens system. Condensers are often corrected for aberration to provide a more precisely aligned beam of light for the objective lens. The focal length of the condenser lens system determines the area of the specimen illuminated by the light coming from it. Various adjustments to the optics of the

Crystal of an antibody-neuraminidase immune complex. The virus from which the neuraminidase protein was purified came from a noddy tern captured on the Great Barrier Reef.
Dr W.G. Laver, Influenza Virus Immunochemistry Laboratory, John Curtin School of Medical Research, ANU.
Photograph Stuart Butterworth.

condenser can be made to provide different effects, such as a dark field illumination, in which the only light entering the objective lens to form the image is that which is scattered or diffracted from the specimen. Under these conditions of illumination the specimen appears brightly lit against a black field. In other optical configurations incident or transmitted light can produce the reversed effect to the dark field image. Incident light illumination is also used to examine opaque subjects. Whatever method of illumination is used, it is essential to have a sufficiently bright source of light focused evenly on to the specimen. The scope of the illuminated field is controlled by a diaphragm which is adjusted to expose an area of light as close in size to the area of the visual field as possible.

There are various specialized optical microscopes which have been developed for particular purposes and which use objective lenses and illumination of a particular mathematical prescription to obtain images of a special character. Phase contrast microscopy is par-

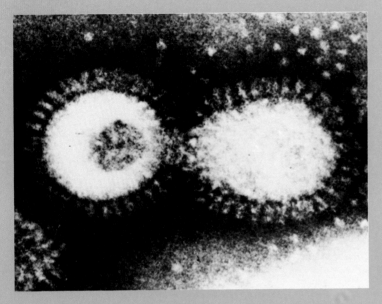

Electronmicrograph of influenza virus particles showing the central core of the virus and its coat comprised of neuraminidase and haemagglutinin. Magnified 200,000 times.
Dr W.G. Laver, Influenza Virus Immunochemistry Laboratory, John Curtin School of Medical Research, ANU.

IMAGES; ILLUSION AND REALITY

ticularly useful for examining living cells without having to have recourse to staining them or altering the optical contrast of their particular parts. While conventional bright-field microscopes produce a visible image of the specimen in terms of light absorption, diffraction and colour differences, transmitted light does not reveal differences in the optical properties of a cell which are influenced by the thickness of structures, their refractive indices and their effect on the light path. With phase microscopic techniques it is possible to examine living cells and investigate their microscopic anatomy by optical means.

The physico-chemical properties of a cell can be interpreted from the extent to which the phase of light waves is displaced by the effects of refractive index and specimen thickness. If this phase displacement can be transduced into changes in brightness then the structures in the cell producing these changes will be visible. The most important attribute of the phase microscope is its capability to differentiate parts of the cell or structures

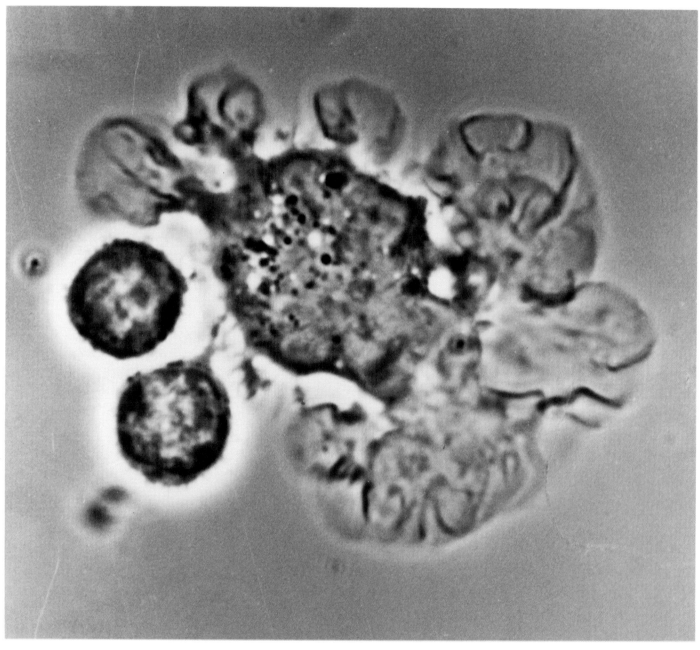

Phase microscope picture of a macrophage and two small lymphocytes in sheep lymph. Bede Morris, Department of Immunology, John Curtin School of Medical Research, ANU.

IMAGES; ILLUSION AND REALITY

within it, which differ by very small degrees of refractive index and thickness. The characteristics of the phase image are built on interference phenomena taking place between two sets of deviated and undeviated light waves. The two sets of light are separated by a condenser diaphragm and a diffraction plate which alter their relative amplitude.

Motion picture phase photomicroscopy is used to study living cells and the dynamics of their movements and progression. The dimensions of the world of the cell are miniaturized not just in relation to space but also in relation to time. If a living cell is viewed under the microscope in real time, its animation is such that it usually appears scarcely to move at all while within the cell, there may be such frenetic Brownian motions that it is impossible to discern any non-random or directed movement in the organelles. The technique of phase-contrast miscroscopy coupled with cinematography allows living cells to be studied within the fourth dimension. If photographic images are taken of a living cell and these

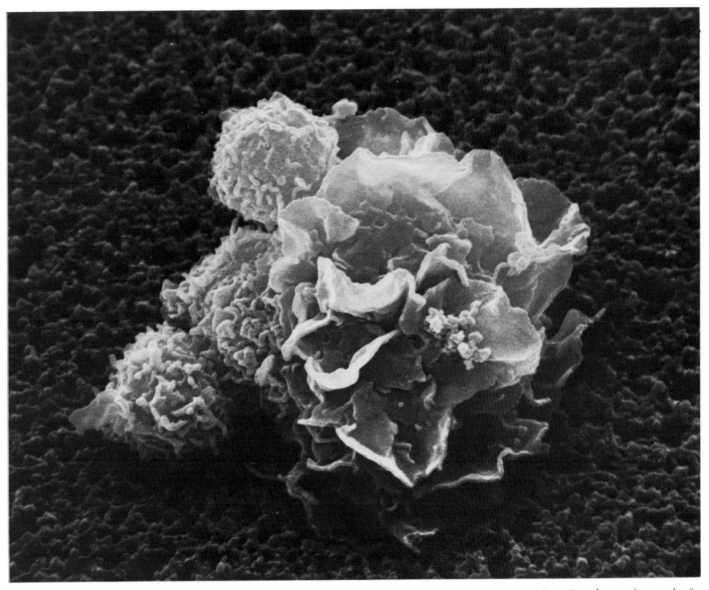

Scanning electromicrograph of a macrophage and two small lymphocytes in sheep lymph. Bede Morris, Department of Immunology, John Curtin School of Medical Research, ANU.

images are then projected more rapidly than they were taken, very slow changes in the perspective of the cell, the movement of its organelles and its progression, can be seen to occur over an interpretable time scale — the cell's activities are 'time-lapsed' so that events which occupy many hours in real time are displayed in minutes or seconds. The developed film can be projected forward or backward to allow retrospective analysis of these elements or it can be stopped to allow analysis of the cell's comportment at a specific moment in time or the effects of substances and interventions on cell behaviour can be studied in relation to other cells. The time-lapsed sequences can be projected on a video-screen or video-recorder so that an instant record or replay of events can be obtained. The life of the cell under study can be re-programmed as if it were caught in a time machine which can rejuvenate it will, arrest its aging process or allow this process to proceed at a slower or faster pace than normal.

Interference microscopy is similar in principle to

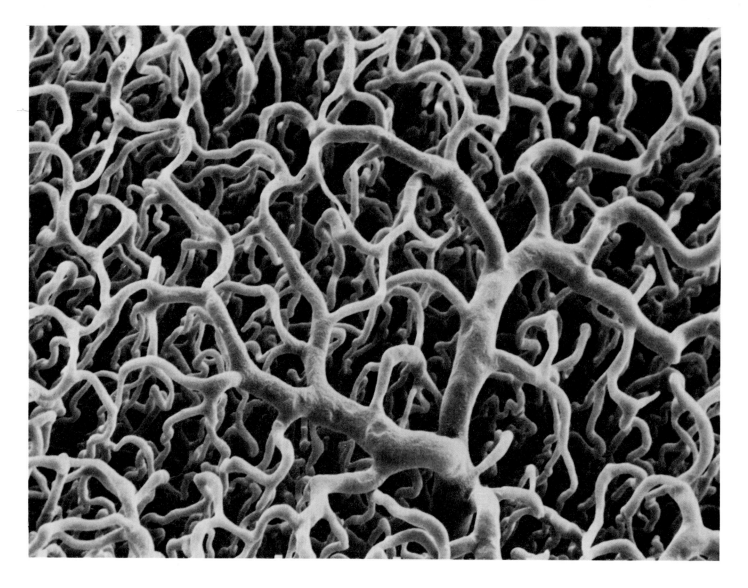

Small blood vessels in the stomach lining of a mouse. Dr G. Schoefl, Cardiovascular, Pathology and Morphology Unit, John Curtin School of Medical Research, ANU.

phase microscopy and is useful for studying unstained objects and preparations which are thicker than those that allow for good image production with the phase microscope. There are two commonly used types of interference microscopes, one which has a split beam system and the other which is a differential shearing interferometer. The split beam system uses an object beam and a reference beam which are then recombined to provide interference patterns of bright and dark lines, similar to the way in which holograms are produced.

The object phase is seen as the displacement of the interference fringes and the relationship between the fringe displacement and the object phase allows the thickness of the specimen to be assessed. The differential shear interference microscope uses reference and object beams that travel the same optical path. The illuminating beam is divided and its two components are then separated by lateral shear. These two separated object beams have a slightly different displacement and interfere with each other. Variations in thickness in the specimen give rise to

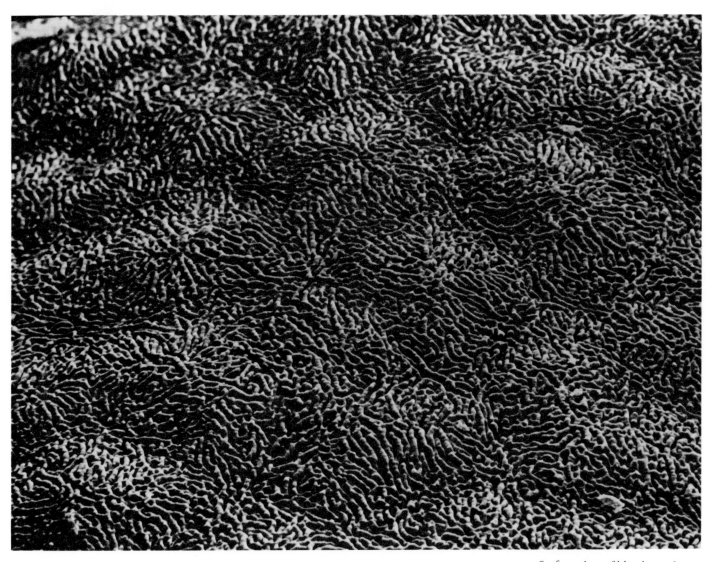

Surface view of blood vessels on the liver.
Dr G. Schoefl, Cardiovascular, Pathology and Morphology Unit, John Curtin School of Medical Research, ANU.

IMAGES; ILLUSION AND REALITY

strong contrast in the image and objects are seen in relief, with depressions appearing as raised areas and vice versa.

Ultra-violet and fluorescence microscopy are two further developments in optical microscopy which are used for enhanced resolution and for the identification of microscopic structures that can be stained by fluorescent dye or be made to fluoresce when excited with short wave-lenght light.

The shorter the wave-length of the light used to illuminate a subject, the greater the theoretical maximum resolving power at the same numerical aperture. There are however, significant difficulties in focusing the image produced by ultraviolet light and it is necessary to record all results photographically or on a television screen, using ultraviolet sensitive television cameras. Monochromatic ultraviolet light can be obtained from mercury vapour lamps combined with appropriate filters for use in fluorescence microscopy. When ultraviolet light is focused onto a specimen, certain components

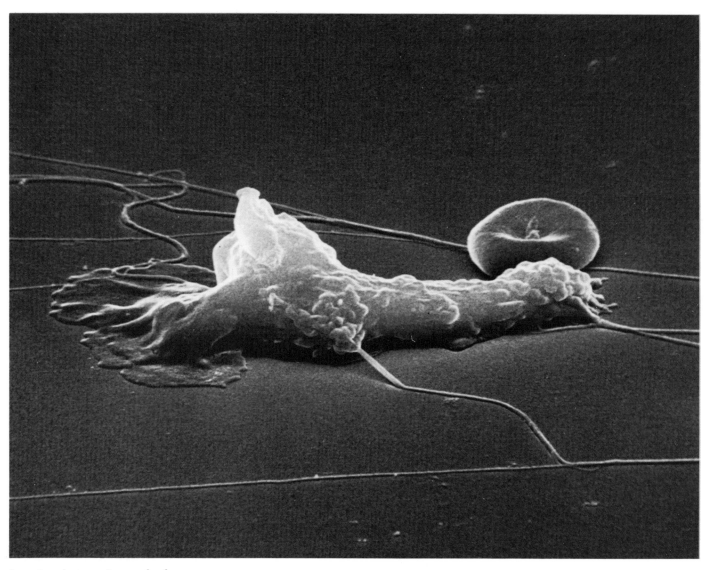

Scanning electronmicrograph of a macrophage and a red cell on glass. The macrophage is spreading itself in an attempt to eat the glass.
Bede Morris, Department of Immunology, John Curtin School of Medical Research, ANU.

IMAGES; ILLUSION AND REALITY

and structures of a particular physical and chemical constitution absorb the energy and re-emit it in a visible form as fluorescence in the visible spectrum.

There are various other microscopic systems which use either different physical principles for manipulating the illuminating beam (reflecting microscopes, polarizing microscopes) or different types of electromagnetic radiation (X-ray microscopes, infra-red microscopes). One particular type of radiation, the electron beam, has been used to develop the electronmicroscope, an instru-

ment of resolving and magnifying powers capable of exploring the dimensions of molecules.

The electronmicroscope

The limit of resolution of a microscope lens is determined by the extent to which the diffraction patterns surrounding two points being viewed overlap one another. The areas of these diffraction patterns are governed by the wave-length of light and by the numerical aperture of the lens. The shorter the wave-length of

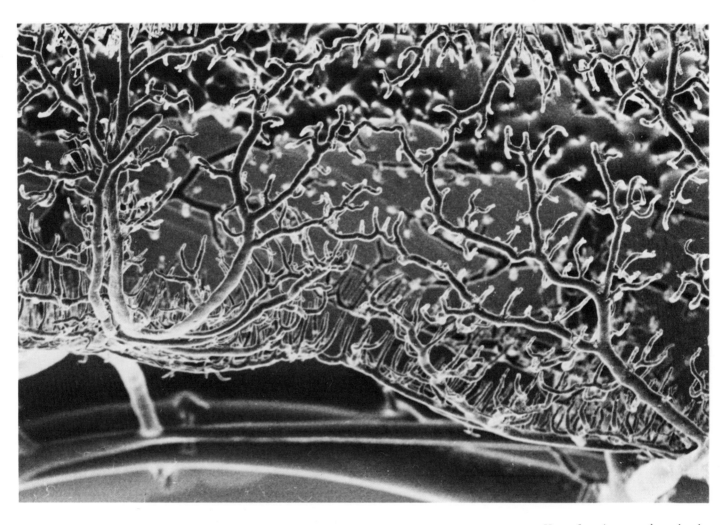

Hoare frost in an apple orchard.

Partially filled blood vessels in mouse intestine.
Dr G. Schoefl, Cardiovascular, Pathology and Morphology Unit, John Curtin School of
· Medical Research, ANU.

the light and the larger the numerical aperture, the greater the resolving power because the diffraction areas around any point will be smaller. The wave-length of visible light extends from 4–8 x 10^{-5} cm. When an object is illuminated with this light the smallest possible distances that can be differentiated are around 2 x 10^{-5} cm. By using ultraviolet light with a wavelength below 3.6 x 10^{-5} cm particles roughly half this size can be photographed. Beyond this the resolution of microscopes using light rays cannot be improved. In bright light, the limit of resolution by the naked eye is about 1/300th cm.

It was well established by the 19th century that light, as the eye records it, is just one part of the electromagnetic spectrum. Discoveries in the first part of the 20th century demonstrated beyond this fact that light, matter and radiation are mutually transformable. It was first suggested in 1924 by Louis de Broglie the French physicist, that electron beams might be regarded as an energy wave-form similar to light. De Broglie calculated the wave-length of electrons accelerated by 60,000 volts

Sheet of epithelial cells from the membrane of a chick embryo.

Dr G. Schoefl, Cardiovascular, Pathology and Morphology Unit, John Curtin School of Medical Research, ANU.

IMAGES; ILLUSION AND REALITY

as being 0.5 x 10⁻⁸ cm. If an electron beam could be generated with these characteristics and used in a microscope instead of a light beam to produce an image, then an enormous increase in magnification and resolving power would be theoretically possible. The image would be produced as a diffraction pattern induced in the beam by a suitable specimen, provided the diffracted electrons could be focused. The electron image would be formed from the pattern of electron scattering induced by atoms in the specimen and image contrast would be determined by the number of high atomic weight atoms present. The first prototype electronmicroscope was developed in 1931 and the first commercial instruments were built in 1935.

The electron beam in an electronmicroscope is focused by an electromagnetic rather than an optical lens. The radial magnetic field provides the lens action constraining the electrons. Electromagnetic lenses have similar characteristics to optical lenses in that they have focal length, a depth of focus, aperture and defects such

Vascular network in the membrane of a chick embryo.

Dr G. Schoefl, Cardiovascular, Pathology and Morphology Unit, John Curtin School of Medical Research, ANU.

as spherical and chromatic aberration and astigmatism. Magnification and focusing are altered by changing the current through the electrical coils associated with the lens. These lenses have a variable focus but the distance between the specimen and the lens does not change. The resolving capabilities of electronmicroscopes, using conventional electromagnetic lenses is around 2×10^{-8}cm.

Scanning electronmicrograph of small lymphocytes in sheep lymph.

Bede Morris, Department of Immunology, John Curtin School of Medical Research, ANU.

Whether it is useful to have powers of resolution beyond this has been debated as the view of the observer is already limited by intermolecular dimensions.

The source of illumination in the electronmicroscope is the electron gun which generates the electron beam. The performance of this gun is critical because it must produce an electron beam of high intensity with a very high voltage and great stability to ensure a narrow spread of wave-length.

The gun itself is similar to the arrangement in a

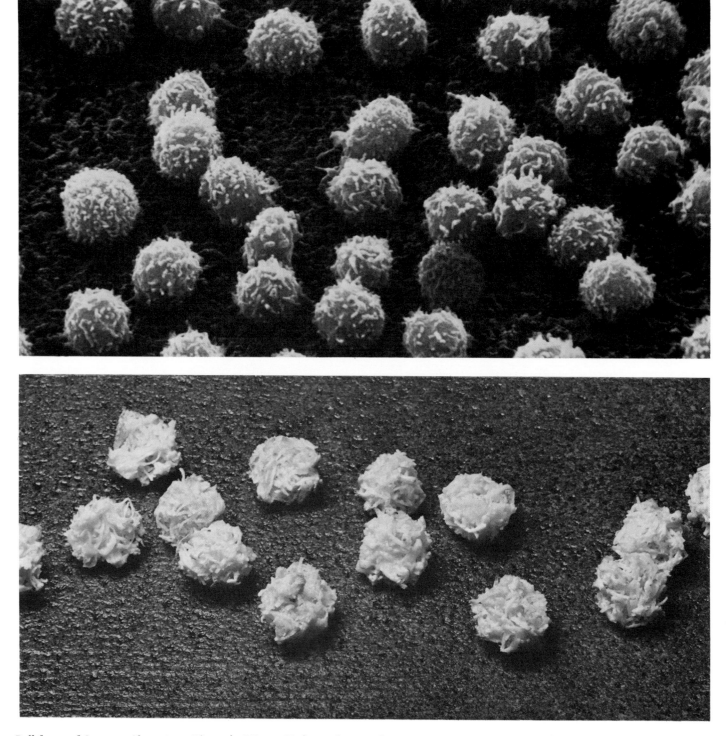

Ball forms of Cocos nucifera.   Picture by Warren Hudson, Photographic Services, John Curtin School of Medical Research, ANU.

IMAGES; ILLUSION AND REALITY

cathode ray tube with a heated tungsten filament from which the electron emission takes place. Electrons are emitted from the insulated cathode which is held at a high negative potential, and they travel towards the anode. The anode is a disc containing an axial hole through which the electrons pass. The condenser lens system brings the beam into convergence onto the object. The characteristics of the electron beam are such that the beam and all components of the system have to be incorporated into a vacuum chamber and the specimen, sup-ported on a copper grid, is introduced into the vacuum chamber on a probe. Operation of the instrument for most practical purposes uses screen magnifications from 500 to 100,000 times.

A visual image of the patterns induced in the electron beam is generated on a phosphorescent screen and this allows the operator to focus onto the specimen. The

Blood vessels in the human heart shown by x-ray photograph.

Dr G. Schoefl, and Dr W. Cliff, Cardiovascular, Pathology and Morphology Unit, John Curtin School of Medical Research, ANU.

screen image tends to have poor contrast and lack sharpness due to the composition of the surface of the phosphor on the screen. The image however, can be recorded photographically to produce a picture of the magnified details of the specimen of high quality. The latent image produced on the photographic film by the electrons can be processed in the usual way, enlarged and enhanced by a variety of techniques. There are two features in the photographic recording of electron beam patterns that are different from light-generated patterns. The differences in film speed and contrast that can be produced with light photography by emulsions of different formulations do not exist with the electron beam. The graininess of the photograph is also a function of electron noise.

Whilst the electronmicroscope has been responsible for revealing the structural detail of cells at very high magnifications, the specimens have to be fixed and examined within a vacuum. The specimens must also be very thin (at least 0.1×10^{-4} cm) to allow adequate penetration of the electrons. Consequently living cells cannot be studied and a stereoscopic interpretation of the structure of the cell is difficult to obtain. The living cell can still only be studied satisfactorily by optical means. High voltage instruments are now in use with accelerating voltages in excess of 1,000,000 volts. The penetration of thicker specimens is possible at these voltages and resolving power is increased by a reduction in spherical and chromatic aberration.

The scanning electronmicroscope was first introduced in the 1950s. With this instrument the electron beam is used to traverse the surface of the specimen, detailing its topography and revealing its surface structure. The probing electron beam discloses the surface structure of the specimen by stimulating the emission of secondary electrons. These electrons are attracted onto a scintillating crystal; the light from this crystal is then fed into a photomultiplier to be amplified as an electrical signal. The electric current modulates the brightness of the display tube which is scanned raster-fashion in synchrony with the electron beam scanning the specimen. The brightness of features on the surface of the specimen coincides essentially with the number of secondary electrons emitted. The specimens must be prepared for scanning electronmicroscopy by dehydration and coating with a material of high electrical conductivity such as gold or platinum.

Little life

The structure of the cell is now revealed as being as complex as the structure of the organism itself. When first viewed under the primitive microscope of Leeuwenhoek, cells were seen to be alive but they appeared as little more than amorphous droplets of protoplasm in which vitality was expressed by an incoherent streaming of the cytoplasm suggesting that it was an unstructured colloid. We now know that the machinery within a cell is an

David Malin

Crystals of salycilglyoxime photographed under crossed polarized light.

IMAGES; ILLUSION AND REALITY

abstraction of the machinery of the organism. The incredible complexity of the cellular digestive system, its musculo-skeleton and its discriminatory mechanisms are just beginning to be understood. But there is no way an understanding of the functions of a cell could have been derived from the results of experiments in biochemistry or biophysics or from metaphysical speculation. Without the microscope and the photograph to establish the form, the function would be uninterpretable.

When the living cell is viewed under the microscope with phase optics, its comportment over time can be related to the comportment of the organism from which the cell came. The isolated cell grows, divides, ages and dies within a time scale which relates to its miniaturized life-history. Marcel Bessis has photographed these activities in blood cells by time-lapse cinemicroscopy,

David Malin
Crystals of ortho-nitrophenol photographed under crossed polarized light.

defining the morphology of cell recognition, cell movement and cell death. The progression of the changes in the tempo of life itself can be related to the life and death of a cell.

> The rhythm of life depends on you
> So slow and cool it seems to be standing still,
> The patient, precious web throbs at your will,
> The rhythm is born, its tempo gentle and sweet

Diamantina river headwaters,
near Kynuna, Queensland.

> Then you are weary, the pace of life grows slow and true
> The grains become drowsy in the peace they always knew.

Jean Bernard.

The death of a cell however does not necessarily compromise the stability of the organism. The multicellular organism retains its form and structure while the cells which comprise it are continually differentiating, migrating, dying and being born. If we put some num-

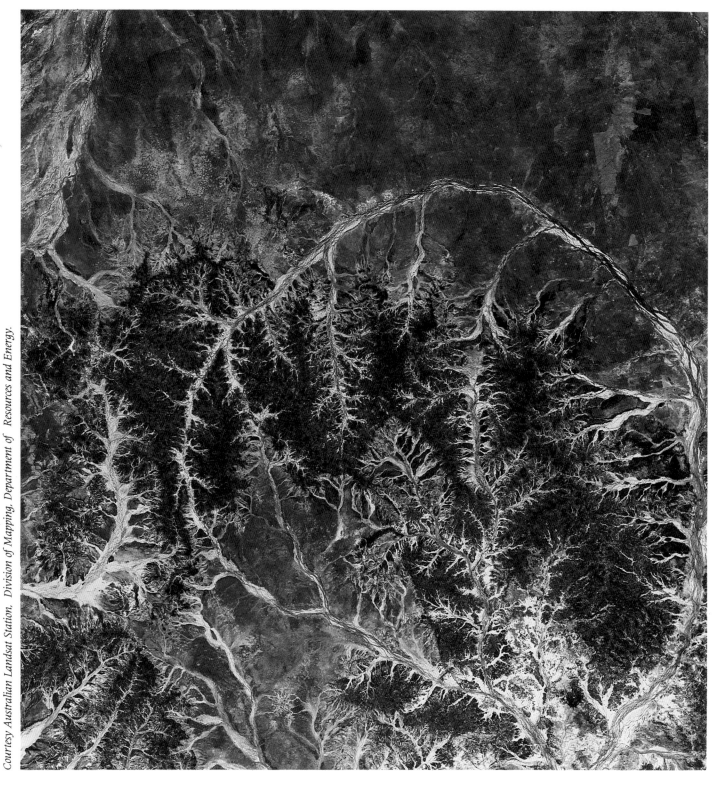

Courtesy Australian Landsat Station. Division of Mapping, Department of Resources and Energy.

False colour image produced from Landsat 2 satellite at 920 km altitude, 5 December 1980.

bers to these processes of cell death and removal, the figures become as incomprehensible and unreal as the numbers which describe the dimensions of the galaxies. Within each of us is a cellular universe every bit as awesome and unbelievable as the world of the stars. The red cells which carry oxygen around the body are about $5–8 \times 10^{-3}$ cm in diameter and they have an average life span of about 120 days, a figure readily understandable and quite believable. It is not so easy to believe that there are 25×10^{12} red cells in the blood (twenty five million,

million cells) and as they only live for 120 days, 2.5×10^6 (2½ million) of them have to be born *each second* to maintain a constant number in the blood. During an average human life 5×10^{18} red cells are made (5 million, million, million).

It is, however, not just the numbers of cells in the blood that present such an incomprehensible statistic. We now know that each nucleated cell in the body car-

Lake Eyre, South Australia,
following summer rains.

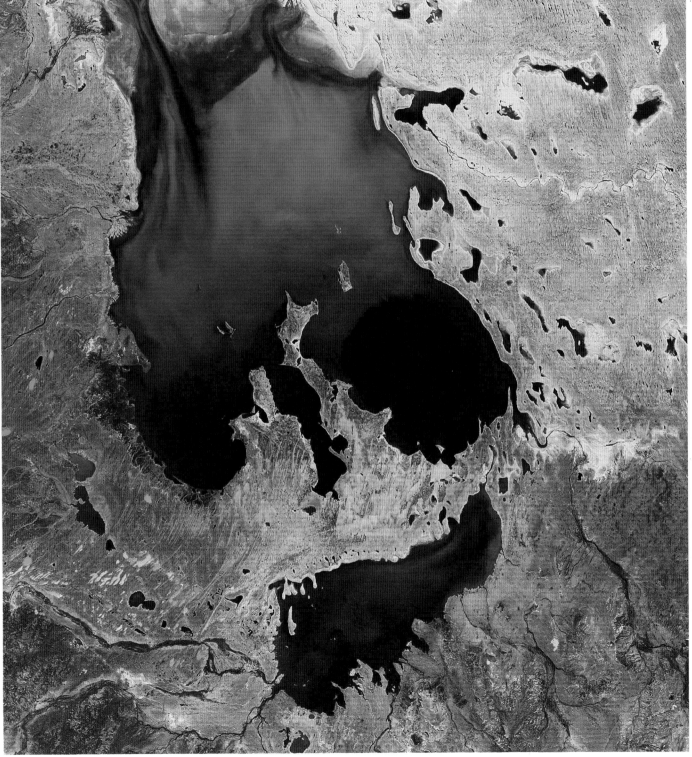

Courtesy Australian Landsat Station, Division of Mapping, Department of Resources and Energy.   Landsat 4 (705 km altitude) 22 February 1984.

ries the complete genetic constitution of both parents, held within a dimension of less than a thousandth of a millimetre. The image of the genetic code is designated as the double helix of the DNA molecule, each strand cross-linked by an ordained sequence of nucleotide bases which spell out instructions for the fabrication of protein molecules. The imagery sees the spiral helix unwinding itself and the code instructing the messenger RNA

molecule to supervise the placement of amino acids in the molecular chain at the correctly specified site. The electronmicroscope reveals the form of the DNA molecule while the X-ray diffraction patterns build for the molecular biologist, an outline of the shape and folding of the molecule. The synthetic and structural machinery of the cell is pictured in terms of organelles such as mitochondria, ribosomes, Golgi apparatus, centrosomes, fibrils, tubules, vacuoles and so forth. A molecular image is constructed for us to understand the

Simpson desert sand dunes and floodwaters of Diamantina river near Birdsville, Queensland.

Landsat 2 (920 km altitude) 6 March 1981.

Courtesy Australian Landsat Station, Division of Mapping, Department of Resources and Energy.

secret of life in images that we can recognize. The cell turns out to have muscles, nerves, bones, joints, and a digestive system just as Leeuwenhoek imagined in 1673. It is an incredible abstraction of its creator — or is it?

The vantage point from which the artist or the scientist chooses to view a circumstance or a result determines the final perception of it. Dog owners think they take their dogs for walks but the reality is different; the dog almost always takes the owner. Likewise we impute intentionality to the actions of the dog who chases a rabbit when the reality is that the hunted compels the hunter to take up the chase — the dog has no option but to follow the rabbit's command. The same view can be held for the sperm, given the sublime task of finding the egg. The male must do what the female commands. Perhaps our view of the cell is wrong too, perhaps it is man who is being used by the cell as a convenient repository for its DNA and to provide it with a mobility it could not have as a free-living organism of itself — perhaps it was a cell not a man that went to the moon!

IMAGES; ILLUSION AND REALITY

Photographing the Stars the Science and Art of Astronomical Photography

What spell is keeping
The stars so steady   D.G. ROSETTI

L.M. Rutherford
Photograph of the moon.
Collodion
1865

SOCIETE FRANCAISE DE PHOTOGRAPHIE

Auguste Bertsch
The eclipse of the moon.
13th October 1856.
Collodion
1856

SOCIETE FRANCAISE DE PHOTOGRAPHIE

IMAGES; ILLUSION AND REALITY

Astronomy is a science in which the subjects of interest are outside any possibility of experimental manipulation or intervention, and except in the most limited sense, are unavailable for any direct experimental encounter or sampling. The only approach that the astronomical scientist can adopt in studying the universe, is to observe the objects of his interest and from these observations, develop his explanatory theories and hypotheses. Visual observation of the stars and other celestial bodies has been the principal way of gathering data from which the past and present can be deduced and the future inferred. Since the middle of the 19th century many of these observations have been made possible by photography.

The life-history of stars is such that their images are historical reconstructions of events long since gone. The stars we see tonight provide a view of the universe in evolution, of worlds in the process of creation and destruction, of a universe that is, that was, and that might be. Stars are formed out of interstellar gas and particulate

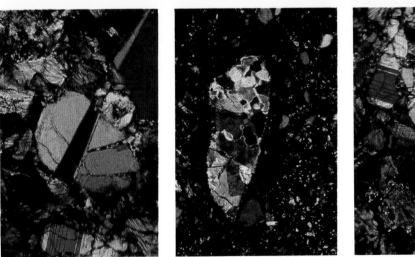

Plagioclase and pyroxene crystals from lunar rock samples of Apollo 12 and 14, viewed under crossed polarized filters.

Photographed by Michael Dugan. Crystals courtesy of NASA and the RSES, Australian National University.

material which coalesce under the influence of gravitational forces. Previously dispersed cosmic matter becomes condensed, leading to the generation of enormously high temperatures within the collapsing cloud as nuclear reactions transform the substance of the star. This formative stage of stellar development may occupy several million years and can be followed by a period of billions of years during which the star is in a relatively stable state. As the content of hydrogen within the star is expended by thermonuclear transformations, the star enters its death throes becoming successively a red giant, perhaps a white dwarf and finally maybe, a black dwarf. Within the universe stars are continually being conceived and born. They develop and die in a progression which can take billions and billions of years. Depending on the star chosen for study we may be looking at any of these periods in its life-history, for we see stars in all stages of evolution. The picture that emerges will also depend on how far away the star is, and how long the light message we record and interpret has taken to reach the earth. The event we see may be recent; in the case of the sun something that happened a few minutes previously; in the case of a close star, something that happened a few years ago, or in the case of a distant star, something that happened 10 or 50 million years ago.

The invention of astronomical telescopes in the 17th century provided the opportunity of observing large numbers of celestial bodies that had previously been invisible to the naked eye. At first the documentation of astronomical phenomena was the main preoccupation of astronomers and this led to the production of charts of the sky in which the dispositions of stars and planets were plotted for all times of the year. This information provided astronomical observers with data to locate objects in much the same way as a terrestrial atlas provides a geographic reference for travellers through details of the relative locations of the oceans and continents. The invention of the telescope also made it possible to view the surface of the moon and adjacent planets directly and map their physical characteristics. When photography was discovered there was an almost immediate acceptance by astronomers of the potential that this new technology offered to the study of the universe, through the documentation and analysis of astronomical events in both space and time. Although the sun and the moon were photographed within a few years of the discovery of the Daguerreotype, it was not until 1883 that an Englishman, Ainslie Common, took the first astronomical photograph which showed objects too faint to be seen by the eye. This marked the beginning of the use of photography as a technique for detection rather than as a technique for documenting the heavens.

In 1887 an international astronomical Conference in Paris decided to construct the first photographic atlas of the heavens. This major enterprise continued for years as the patterns of stars, down to the 14th magnitude of brightness, were calculated and recorded. It was a work of such enormous scope and the number of stars recorded so great, that the atlas has never been completed in the form that the enthusiasts at the Conference envisaged. It was just too difficult and time consuming to do by measuring manually the thousands of images on the photographic plates. Today, wide-field Schmidt telescopes have so reduced the time required to map the sky photographically that there are now comprehensive atlases of the heavens which shows the positions of stars as faint as magnitude 21. There are now available photographic reference catalogues for the bright galaxies, for clusters of galaxies, for peculiar galaxies and for the morphology of galaxies. Maps of the sky are now being constructed of objects 'seen' by nonvisual radiation such as X-rays, radiowaves, infra-red and ultra-violet rays. Lunar atlases of incredible quality and detail have been produced from photographs taken through high power telescopes. More recently, photographs taken from satellites such as the Lunar Orbiter, have charted the moon in such precise detail at scales of 1:100,000 that the first astronauts had the comfort of arriving at their destination knowing exactly the nature of the terrain on which they would take their first steps.

Photography has provided the first quantitative means of studying the physical characteristics of stars, planets and nebulae through the spectroscopic analysis of their electromagnetic radiations. Because of the unfathomable dimensions of the universe, the only way the stars and dust clouds can be studied is through the energy that is emitted by them. To do this presents certain problems because much of the stellar radiation which is directed towards the earth's surface is absorbed by its atmospheric envelope. The atmosphere however is not completely opaque and it has areas of relative clarity which can serve as windows through which to view the heavens. Light and some infra-red waves are able to penetrate the earth's atmosphere relatively readily, but in doing so, they are bent and perturbed by atmospheric turbulence, while halation and scintillation degrade the sharpness of the image of the object from which they originate.

The light emitted by a star has always to be disassociated from the luminiferous noise of contaminating radiant objects in the night sky to obtain analytical data concerning the nature and origin of the light. While this does not present any problems when observing bright stars, it is a significant limitation for photometry and photography of faint stars and cosmic phenomena whose brightness approximates the general level of light in the sky. Over the past 50 years an array of highly sophisticated techniques has been developed for making observations of astronomical phenomena that were previously indescribable. These techniques include methods for analyzing radiowaves, X-rays, infra-red and ultra-violet radiation as well as visible light. Some of these

IMAGES; ILLUSION AND REALITY

techniques depend on the conversion of the recorded energy waves to photographic images as well as using the photographic process itself to detect cosmic radiation by the tracks these particles make when they strike a photographic plate. Photography has for a long time been the primary method for recording observations made with the optical telescope despite the advent of electronic detectors and it remains one of the most widely used methods for astronomical research.

Techniques in Astronomical Photography

The principal use of photography in the study of astronomy is to record cumulatively, the light emitted from extremely faint celestial objects, orders of magnitude fainter than anything the unaided eye could possible see.

Full moon photo, Lick Observatory, University of California, Santa Cruz showing prominent rays from Tycho crater, due to material thrown out during the massive asteroid impact forming the crater.

IMAGES; ILLUSION AND REALITY

The astronomer's camera and telescope are attached to an instrument which traverses the sky to maintain their common optical axis stationary in relation to the stars as the earth rotates. This alignment is crucial because the exposure required to record the light of extremely faint stars may run into an hour or more. The emulsion used has to be highly sensitive to light, and the telescope must ideally be of short focal length and large aperture. Schmidt cameras have focal lengths approaching f/1 or less and are able to photograph an area of sky 6 degrees or more in diameter.

Astronomical objects of interest are mostly self-luminous and the photographer cannot alter or influence their arrangement in space relative to other objects or adjust their relative brightness. The surface brightness of these subjects varies over a range of 20 magnitudes, a variation of a hundred million fold. The recorded photograph is a result which may contain 10^9 bits of information on the luminosity, the colour and the position of countless numbers of objects. This information can be extracted and analyzed in many different ways.

The characteristics of the photographic plate are important in determining the quality of the astronomical image obtained and as light intensities are often very low, fast, highly sensitive emulsions are used. The speed of the emulsion can be enhanced (hypersensitized) by baking the plates in nitrogen followed by hydrogen for a few hours at room temperature. This technique reduces exposure times by a factor from 3 to 20, depending on the type of emulsion.

Because much of astronomy is concerned with faint image photography, the emulsions used give high contrast pictures which are developed to a high density. The full density range of such pictures can be explored by a technique of unsharp marking which suppresses those parts of the image which have a large-scale, low information content while at the same time, the fine detail of the picture can be enhanced. In addition extremely faint objects can be revealed by photographic amplification procedures. Such a procedure allows features about 0.5% as faint as the night sky to be detected. In effect this means that with such methods the photographic plate is able to distinguish 1 signal photon coming from the object of interest from 200 noise photons coming from the glow of the night sky. The photographic amplification process enhances the apparent size of the silver grains which form the original image, and the picture appears more grainy. To reduce this effect and to improve detection of the faint light source, several different plates of the same object can be added together and superimposed on one another in a registration frame.

Apart from observing and photographing stars through the telescope, their constitution and their velocity can be assessed by spectroscopic analysis of the characteristics of the light emitted from them. The spectra of the light emitted from a star can be recorded on a photographic plate and its specific components analyzed. This provides information about the elements present and the chemical composition of the star and tells something of the movement of the star in space (its radial velocity) and its temperature. This information has been used to provide evidence of the origin and evolutionary history of stars, planets and nebulae.

There are certain optical limitations to photographic spectroscopy which relate to the capacity of photographic emulsions to record light in the infra-red part of the spectrum and the sensitivity of the photographic plates necessary to register the various spectral components of light coming from extremely faint objects. The fainter a star is, the less the spectrum of the light coming from it can be dispersed to produce a photographic image. This greatly affects spectral resolution. In the case of the sun, a star of average luminosity but very close proximity, copious amounts of light are available for analysis so that the solar spectrum, originating from discrete parts of the surface of the sun, can be analyzed in great detail. By restricting the light emission onto the photographic plate to well-defined spectral bands by the use of narrow band filters, the photographic features of the sun and planets and the emission characteristics of their radiation can be analyzed.

Colour photographs disclose colours in starlight that cannot be seen directly because even with the largest telescope, the intensity of the light emission is too low to stimulate the colour receptive mechanisms of the eye. The problems inherent in astronomical photography are compounded when colour images are required, because there are no commercially produced colour films which meet the particular and peculiar requirements of astronomers. Suitable colour systems have to be devised for the particular purposes required.

Several important and novel, colour photographic processes have been developed by David Malin of the Anglo Australian Telescope for the production of colour photographs of the stars. The principal steps in colour rendition depend on an additive, three colour printing technique, based on Maxwell's original (1861) methods but using modern colour film materials. Three primary colour separations are taken and then superimposed precisely on one another. Malin has also developed a method of incorporating information on colour balance on monochrome plates. This is essential when the colours of the photographic subject are completely unknown and invisible to the eye. The colours must be recreated in the darkroom through the use of well-established, standardized, astronomical emulsions and filter combinations which are used as reference sources for the colour images. The colour photographic process can include an enhancement technique to reveal the very faintest images ever detected in astronomy.

IMAGES; ILLUSION AND REALITY

Astronomical Photography and Art

'Had I been present at the birth of this planet I would probably not have believed on the word of an Archangel that the blazing mass, the incandescent whirlpool there before our eyes at a temperature of 50 million degrees would presently set about the establishment of empires and civilizations, that it was on its way to produce Greek art and Italian painting.'
W. MacNeil Dixon, *The human situation*

We now know that the fundamental constituents of the stars are represented in the fundamental constituents of the earth and the other planets. Each different atomic species in the universe is related to every other, and as a consequence, there is an evolutionary commonality between every animate and inanimate object within the universe. Not only are all humans related, in an

A composite picture of the moon at first and third quarter taken in 1936 by the Lick Observatory, University of California, Santa Cruz. (Note; the shadows point in opposing directions). Compare this with the full moon photo to see the effect of sun angle in the surface features.

evolutionary sense, to one another, but they are also related to all other forms of life, and eventually through organic and inorganic non-living material, to the primordial atomic particles.

The idea of a progressive cosmic evolution from the most primitive atom, hydrogen, to a self-replicating DNA molecule, to a living cell, to a human being is not easily understood. We cannot appreciate chance and probability operating within the time scale of billions and billions of years when our own existence is so caducous.

'When we compare the present life of man with that time of which we have no knowledge, it seems to me like the swift flight of the lone sparrow through the banqueting hall where you sit in the winter months . . . The sparrow flies swiftly in through one door of the hall and out through another . . . Similarly man appears on earth for a little while, but we know nothing of what went on before this life, or what follows.'
The Venerable Bede
History of the English Church and People

David Malin
The Horsehead Nebula in Orion
Only a few degrees away from the spectacular Orion Nebula, which can be seen with the unaided eyes, the Horsehead Nebula is by contrast difficult to find, even with a large telescope. Nonetheless this curious dark nebula is one of the best-known images in astronomy, probably because of its chance likeness to a recognisable form. The horsehead shape is an extension to a substantial cloud of dark obscuring material which fills the lower part of the picture and hides the light of stars beyond. The outer surface of the dusty gas is illuminated by Sigma Orionis which is off the top of the picture and which causes the hydrogen gas there to glow distinctly red, outlining the horsehead shape. Here and there bright stars are partially enveloped in the dust cloud and their scattered light is seen as an irregular blue reflection nebula.

IMAGES; ILLUSION AND REALITY

The difficulty in thinking about the universe, its origins and its evolution relates to its scale. The mensuration of the cosmic world is such that the human mind can understand it only as an abstraction. The distances, timescale and numbers involved, are incomprehensible and totally irrelevant for an organism whose life-span of three score years and ten is an infinitesimal and insignificant interlude in the cosmic evolution. The only hope man has of comprehending the universe, is to place himself somewhere within the creative master plan. Man's involvement in the study of the universe and his attempt to understand the physical and mathematical laws which govern it, are part of this human aspiration to know the origins and meaning of life and the natural world, and man's part in it.

The dimensions of the universe cannot be described by any conventional scale of measurement because the distances involved in relating stars to one another and to the earth and the sun, lie outside the timewarp of a human life. Countless billions of stars, with countless

David Malin
The Helix nebula, NGC 7293
This faint object is the nearest planetary nebula to us and on deep photographs has a diameter of about half a degree — the same apparent size as the Moon in the sky. The AAT colour picture shows the various ionisation levels within the shell of matter ejected from the central star, the greenish middle portion being due to ionised oxygen, the outer red due to nitrogen and hydrogen. The smallest radial blobs inside the red shell are thought to be 150 astronomical units across (150 times the earth-sun distance) and they give this beautiful object its alternative name, the Sunflower Nebula. The Helix is at a distance of about 400 light years from Earth.

billions of planets, in countless billions of galaxies, exist within a void so vast that they occupy a trivial amount of its space; the universe is in fact almost empty. And while we know that a billion is a very large number, a billion billion is something else again. We would need almost a billion life-times to count such a number even if we devoted the whole of our time to it. Yet we have to come to grips, in some way, with numbers and dimensions of this and even greater magnitude if we are to have any idea of the astronomical world. We can really only do this by analogy and abstraction and by using an artistic perception of the universe to help interpret the uninterpretable.

The science of astronomy is concerned with providing a physical and mathematical basis on which to build an understanding of the universe, its stellar demography, and its evolution. However few of us are as comfortable with the implications of the symbols of Einstein's equation of general relativity, as we are with a picture of the night sky and its stars and a descriptive caption telling us

David Malin
*Reflection Nebula in Orion,
NGC 1973, 75, 77*
If it was anywhere else in the sky, this nebula would be regarded as a magnificent spectacle. However this group of stars and its nebulosity is just half a degree — the apparent size of the full moon — north of the much brighter Orion Nebula and has largely been ignored because of it. The group of hot stars here are seen with the unaided eye as a single object, the northernmost star in the sword of Orion. Most of the nebulosity is light from the group of stars deflected by dust particles which preferentially scatter blue light. Some of these stars are sufficiently hot to excite the hydrogen gas which pervades the region and creates the distinctive red glow. Together, the stars and nebula create an impression of quiet beauty quite unlike the maelstrom of the adjacent Orion Nebula.

what the multitude of bright spots means. Knowing that e=mc² does not make the dimensions of the universe any more comprehensible or believable for most people. We have need of a pictorial reference in our minds to create the imagined reality of the universe. So we have pictured in our minds the rings of Saturn and Uranus, the "canals" of Mars, the moon with its old man and his bundle of sticks or, for the gourmet, a lunar constitution of green cheese. The point of view is of course all important in determining the illusion that a star or a pattern of stars creates in mind of the viewer. The constellation which evoked the image of a great bear in the minds of the Greeks who saw it in the night sky, appeared to the North American Indians as a pot with a long handle, a big dipper; the English, more agriculturally moved, saw it as a plough or a hay cart while the French inevitably thought of it as a casserole. Humans have seen the sky filled with extraordinary objects, illusory representations of our artistic minds; crabs, birds, archers, lions, bulls and so forth. Astronomy has repudiated the idea that the sky

David Malin
The Pleiades Cluster (ROE 18)
The Pleiades cluster is a group of many hundreds of stars about 400 light years from Earth in the northern constellation of Taurus. The cluster has been recognised since ancient times and seven of the brightest stars bear the names of seven sisters, the daughters of Atlas. These seven are easy to see with the unaided eye but keen-sighted observers can count up to about a dozen.

The extensive nebulosity is difficult to see in a telescope of any size and is best recorded photographically.

The Pleiades cluster has not existed long on the Galactic time scale, perhaps 50 million years. Even so the colours of the brighter stars indicate that they have already consumed much of their hydrogen fuel and are moving towards the end of their lives. The fainter stars are less profiligate and will continue to shine much as they do now long after their highly luminous companions have burned themselves out.

is full of mythological creatures but the sophistry of cosmic physics still has use for naive and ingenuous dispositions to communicate and explain these stupendous cosmic phenomena. Astrophysicists do not talk in terms of the signs of the Zodiac any more; they have replaced the crab and the lion with black holes, red giants and white dwarfs. However for all this, a black hole is still an astrophysical phenomenon which is incomprehensible without an image and a descriptive caption. If the caption is withheld from the viewer, an astronomical picture can conjure up a range of possibilities, many of which have no relation to its origins. If we look at photographs of some of the more celebrated nebulae and supernovae, the colours in the reflected light from their cosmic dust, create images of breathtaking beauty that are artistic compositions in their own right. The abstract patterns caused by diffraction and reflection and the spectral colours produced by the thermonuclear transformations can easily be seen as the expression of a cosmic Artist of infinite talent.

David Malin
The Orion Nebula (ROE 8)
It is the proximity of the Orion Nebula rather than its size which is mainly responsible for its spectacular appearance. Many other much larger nebulae are known, but none offer us so intimate a view of a stellar nursery. The nebula is visible to the unaided eye as a misty patch around the central star of the line of three which form Orion's sword. Binoculars or a modest telescope will show that these three 'stars' are easily resolved into loose groups of three or four individuals which can be seen in this photograph. The central group of stars, known as The Trapezium Cluster, is hidden in the glow of the Nebula in this photograph. In reality these stars are responsible for the nebula, for without them little would be visible here. Conversely, the high concentration of dust and gas in this part of the sky has resulted in the formation of the stars . Thus the evolution of the stars and nebulae goes hand in hand.

Right
David Malin
The Spiral Galaxy, M83 (NGC5236)
M83 is thought to be very like our own Galaxy, but seen from above and at a distance of 27 million light years. Composed of millions of stars and clouds of dust this object is one of the finest examples of spiral galaxies, and shows a concentration of older yellow stars in its central nucleus with younger, blue stars and patchy clouds of glowing gas in the trailing spiral arms. The massive blue stars occasionally explode as supernovae which are seen in M83 every 10 or 15 years, more frequently than in any other galaxy.

IMAGES; ILLUSION AND REALITY

It is logical to disqualify these erroneous interpretations of the universe based on illusion; the reality of the moon is dust, sand and boulders not green cheese, for man has been there and shown it to be so. But man has never been anywhere else in our solar system, let alone to other places beyond this parochial dimension. No matter if we knew with absolute certainty that the universe existed within two, three or four dimensional space, that there are other universes beyond our own or that there is an infinite hierarchy of universes like the Russian dolls, each one resembling the other but locked within the dimensions of its hierarchical predecessor, we would still see that universe planned around ourselves. We must still interpret its beginnings, its present and its end in terms of our own lives and within our own minds. The artist in each of us transforms the elements of life into dreams and hopes; we must believe that there is something better to come in the future; without this hope, the creative force within us, our personal sun, would be extinguished.

IMAGES; ILLUSION AND REALITY

The last two images in this book tell something of the story of photography and its contributions to human knowledge so far. These images define the dimensions of human awareness from the molecule to infinity. At the molecular level we have a picture which entails the entire evolutionary history of life on earth, its past, present and its future. The pictorial abstraction of human civilization is in the tortured coils of the DNA molecule representing as it does Nature's most recent prototype of

DNA of Baker's or Brewer's Yeast (*Saccharomyces cerevisiae*).

Transmission electronmicrograph. courtesy of Des Clark-Walker, Department of Genetics, Research School of Biological Sciences, ANU.

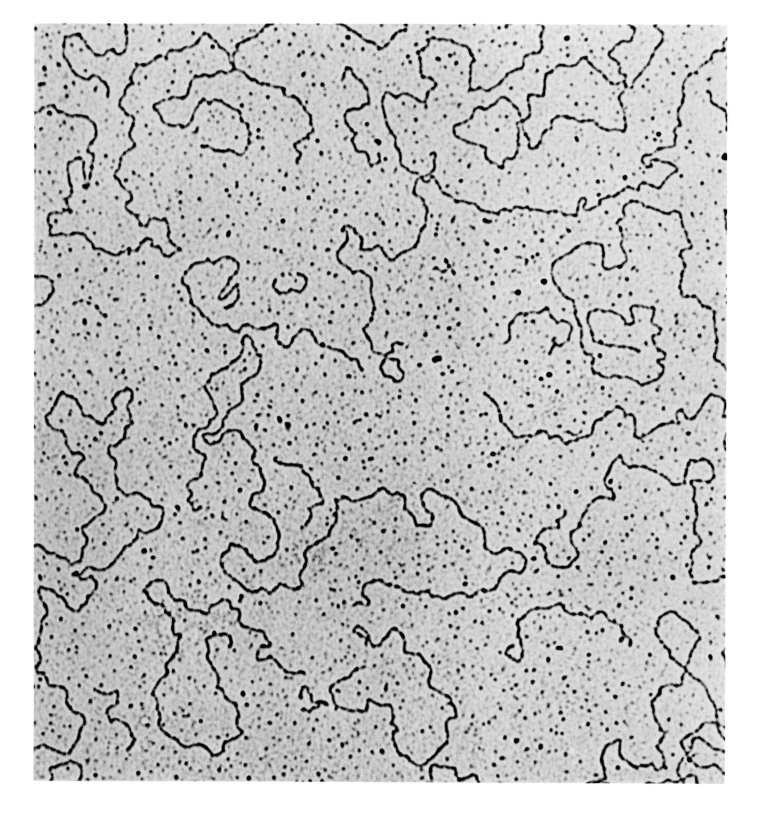

IMAGES; ILLUSION AND REALITY

the species. The picture of a cluster of galaxies in deep space reveals the countless numbers of solar systems, in countless numbers of galaxies, extending into infinity and beyond. However it doesn't end here. The infinite dimension of the universe with its infinite population of solar systems and galaxies seems almost certain to have allowed for the emergence, somewhere, of life forms other than those we know on earth. This is not to stretch chance and probability all that far beyond what we know has already happened. And so having eaten the apple we must continue to reach for the true meaning of this unbelievable yet acknowledged game of chance.

David Malin
A cluster of galaxies.

Biographies

ADRIEN

Industrial engineer, member of the French Photographic Society and member of the Photo Club of Paris. The Club was founded by Demachy and Puyo who were responsible for the French 'pictorial movement'. Adrien was one of many photographers who abandoned black and white photography when the Lumière brothers developed and marketed their autochrome plates in 1905.

AGUADO, Count Olympe 1827–1894

Foundation member of the Heliographic Society, Foundation member of the French Photographic Society. Aguado was the son of a famous art collector, the Marquis Las Marismas; he learned his photography from Viscomte Vigier, a Foundation member of the French Photographic Society. Aguado had a very successful photographic studio in the bd des Italiens where he employed several photographic assistants. His studio became a meeting place for famous photographers of the day. Aguado was one of the first photographers to use the albumin process and to make print enlargements from negatives.

ALBERT, Joseph 1825–1886

Appointed photographer to the court of Maximillian II Emperor of Austria in 1855. Albert invented the 'Albertype', a mechanical photographic procedure in 1867. This was a special press which enabled multiple large prints to be made from one negative. Albert specialised in large-scale photographs, and his printing process allowed him to produce daily, 100 large size photographs of superior quality.

During the 1870 war between France and Germany, the 'Albertype' was used to print the maps used by the German army. Albert was awarded the Prussian military medal for his invention as well as many gold and silver medals for his remarkable photographic exhibits.

ALEXANDER 1927– .

Alexander was born in London and studied at St Martin's School of Art. His work has concentrated on abstract sculptural pieces of enormous scale. Some of his commissions such as the *Jubilee Oracle* for the South Bank London, *The Great Tower* for Rutland Water and *Duet* for University Hospital, Nottingham are artistic and constructional works of prodigious size and mass. In 1980 Alexander began developing an entirely new form of 'four dimensional sculpture' in which the fourth dimension was provided by the perceptual interpretation of the viewer. In 1982 Alexander had the idea of extending his four dimensional sculptures using a light medium provided by lasers. At this time he began an association with Hariharan of CSIRO seeking ways of interpreting these 4 dimensional

sculptures as holograms. Alexander worked with Hariharan as artist in residence in 1984–85 developing further the techniques of holographic sculpture, adapting Hariharan's techniques in optical physics to the production of holograms that can be viewed with ambient light. In June 1985 Alexander produced the world's largest holograms (2 metres x 1.5 metres) in a laboratory in Los Angeles. These are white light transmission holograms and stereograms of enormous visual and sensual impact and represent transitional forms of holographic art as significant as the first Calotypes of Fox Talbot were in the evolution of photography.

ARCHER, Frederick Scott 1813–1857

The inventor of the *collodion process* whereby silver salts were incorporated into a solution of gun-cotton, alcohol and ether and coated onto glass plates. His first photographs on collodion-coated glass plates were done in September 1850 but it was not until March 1851 that he published the details of the process. Archer never received the recognition due to him for this very significant development in photographic technology. The *collodion era* of French photography was to last for nearly forty years. While the process made fortunes for a large number of manufacturers, Scott Archer died in poverty in May 1857. A national appeal was set up in England after his death to provide money to support his family.

BAYARD, Hippolyte 1801–1881

Foundation member of the French Photographic Society. Early in 1839, Bayard made some direct positive photographs with the camera obscura using paper sensitized with silver chloride and treated with potassium iodide to produce the photographic image. He showed these photographs on June 24, 1839 at an art exhibition organised to raise funds for disaster victims of Martinique. This exhibition was held 56 days before Daguerre's discovery was made public, on August 19, 1839. Bayard's photographs were thus the first to be shown publicly. He submitted a sealed envelope to the Academie des Sciences on November 8 1839 in which he described his process for the development of the latent image on paper using mercury vapour. Bayard's publication thus preceded Fox Talbot's description of this process. Bayard was also a foundation member of the Heliographic Society and he took an active part in the Society's work. In 1851, he developed a procedure which made his positive photographic papers more sensitive. Later he was one of the first to use large size albumin plates. In collaboration with Count Aguado, Bayard developed methods for making photographic enlargements. Bayard's contributions to photography were of a comparable significance to those of Niépce, Daguerre and Talbot. He became Secretary-General of the French Photographic Society in 1865, and served in this post until 1881 when he retired to Nemours.

BERTSCH, Auguste

Foundation member of the French Photographic Society, Bertsch gave many lectures and seminars at its meetings describing his work on instantaneous photographic methods, photomicroscopy, photographic enlargement, dark room design etc. He was elected a Chevalier of the Imperial order of the Legion d'Honneur for his photographic discoveries and their application to science. In collaboration with Camille D'Arnaud, the then Director of the magazine *L'Artiste*, Bertsch opened a portrait studio in Paris. He disappeared in 1871 during the German siege of Paris and was not seen again.

BISSON Bros, Auguste and Louis

Amongst the earliest photographic portraitists the Bissons improved the sensitivity of the daguerrean iodide plate by coating it with a mixture of bromine and iodine chloride. They presented the results of their studies to the Academie des Sciences in 1841. Dr Dumoutier used the processes developed by the Bissons to photograph the different anthropological races during his voyage around the world with Admiral Dumont-Durville in 1842. Two hundred of Dumoutier's Daguerrotypes were reproduced as lithographs by the Bisson Bros for official government publications. From 1842 to 1851 the Bissons further developed the daguerreotype process: they gilded the plates to give them colour and durability, they used electrolysis to coat plates with silver and developed colour filters for their cameras. From 1849 to 1851 the Bisson brothers took the portraits of all 900 members of the French National Assembly and produced a series of 40 lithographs from these Daguerrotypes. Their studio was a very elegant affair located in the bd des Italiens where Le Gray also had a studio. Prominent authors and artists of the day used it as a meeting place. Amongst the more notable works done by the Bissons from 1851 were their photographs of Rembrandt's and Durer's paintings in the National Library and their photographs of the principal monuments of Paris. The latter were done in large format up to 48 x 38 cm. In 1855 they scaled Mont-Blanc, and took a photographic record of the climb. Auguste Bisson repeated the climb in July 1861 and he took 25 porters with him to carry all his heavy photographic equipment.

BLANQUART-EVRARD, Louis Desiré

A cloth merchant of Lille and a painter of miniatures on ivory. Blanquart-Evrard became interested in photography in 1844 after learning of the negative-positive paper process of Talbot. In 1847 Blanquart-Evrard developed a negative process using impregnated paper moistened before use with an acid solution of silver nitrate. In 1851 he founded, at Loos-les-Lille in the north of France, a business called 'The Photographic Press' which produced photographic prints commercially.

The business lasted for five years before it closed but in this time it produced an admirable series of photographs on architecture, sculpture, painting and the archaeology of the Middle-East. Close to 100,000 photographs were produced of which only around a thousand remain. Blanquart-Evrard published a number of books on photography; *The Photographic Album of the Artist and the Amateur, Photographs of Paris* and later *Egypt, Nubia, Palestine and Syria*. The latter book contained photographs collected in 1849–1850–1851 by Maxime du Camp. He also published *The Nile — Monuments and Landscapes* by J.B. Green and *Views of Jerusalem* by Salzmann in 1855. These books contained the original photographs glued onto velum. After 'The Photographic Press' closed in 1855 Blanquart-Evrard worked in collaboration with Thomas Sutton in a new printing works at St Brelade's Bay, Jersey. Eighteen publications were produced at this establishment.

DAGUERRE, Louis Jacques Mandé 1787–1851

Artist, painter, theatrical designer. Daguerre started work with Degotis, the painter and set designer for the Paris Opera. He then worked as set designer at the Ambigu Comique theatre. In collaboration with Charles Bouton, he created the Diorama, displayed to the public at the Place du Château d'Eau in Paris, now the Place de la Republique. It depicted scenes painted on a semi-transparent gauze screen which were animated by special lighting effects. Objects were placed in the front of the scene to give the whole Diorama an impeccable detail and dimensional perspective. The spectacle was very popular with the Parisian public and Daguerre, in order to achieve the maximum reality, made use of the camera obscura in drafting the images for the Diorama. In 1826, he was sponsored by the optician Charles Chevalier to work on methods of fixing the photographic image, a problem that had already been tackled by Nièpce in 1816. An association was formed between Daguerre and Nièpce in 1829 after some initial difficulties due to Nièpce's suspicions of Daguerre. The pooled resources of the collaboration led to significant improvements in the photographic process. The collaborative agreement involved the disclosure by Nièpce of 'all the details of his process' while Daguerre was required to disclose all the refinements of his dark room techniques. Daguerre's contribution to the partnership was significantly less than that of Nièpce for his knowledge of photochemistry was rudimentary. Daguerre's attempts to improve Nièpce's heliographic process were unsuccessful. The partnership ended with the death of Nièpce in 1833. Subsequently Daguerre, helped in all likelihood by some of his scientific colleagues, perfected the daguerreotype process in which photographs were produced directly onto silver plates. The real achievement of Daguerre was, without doubt, his discovery of the formation of the latent image on sensitized plates exposed to light and the method of developing this image to make it visible. In 1837 he succeeded in fixing the latent image with a solution of sodium chloride. In 1839, with the help and patronage of the influential physicist Francois Arago, the rights to the daguerreotype process were purchased by the French government and offered to the world. Daguerre received for his Daguerreotype and Diorama inventions an annual pension of 6,000 francs. The only son of Nièpce, Isidore who succeeded his father in partnership with Daguerre received 4,000 francs.

DAWSON, Paula 1954– .

Born in Brisbane, Paula Dawson trained as an art teacher at Melbourne State College, specializing in sculpture and in the use of laser light to portray reflections of images and forms. She became interested in holography in 1975 and in its potential as an art medium and began a study of optical physics in relation to holography. Subsequently in 1979, she went to the Laboratory de Physique et Optique at Besancon in France where she worked with Dr Nicole Abischer the inventor of animated holography. On her return to Australia in 1980 she took up teaching sculpture at the Prahran College of Art. She returned to Besancon in 1980 where she produced a hologram of a lounge room, the largest holographic image so far recorded. Paula Dawson was commissioned in 1984 to produce a hologram suitable for the Australian Pavillion at Tsukuba as part of the Expo 85. This resulted in her constructing the Eidola Suite comprising three primary laser transmission images of the largest spaces so far documented by holography.

DELARCHE

Delarche exhibited a series of original photographs of plants and flowers in natural colour at the Annual General Meeting of the French Photographic Society on June 4 1875. 'I use the plant itself as a picture to obtain my proof. I treat it in a special chemical bath to colour it — I have one bath for yellow and another for green. The other colours are obtained by chemicals but they are applied with brush strokes'. Delarche's process was not developed further.

DELONDRE, Paul

Paris lawyer, member of the French Photographic Society from 1856. One of the last photographers to use the calotype process (1860). Delondre took part in many photographic exhibitions organised by the French Photographic Society.

DEMACHY, Robert 1859–1936

Son of a banking family, Demachy was a wealthy amateur photographer who devoted his life to the study of music, design, and photography, leaving his older brother to manage the family bank. He became a member of the French Photographic Society in 1882 and the Photo Club of Paris in 1890. It was through his associations with the Photo Club that his work became best known. He was immediately attracted to the pictorialist school and with Puyo was acknowledged one of the leaders of this movement. His success as a photographer was incontestable and was acknowledged even by the critics of pictorialism. His work was accepted by the Royal Photographic Society of London, an organisation known for its conservative attitudes and published in the review *Camera Work*, a publication run by Stieglitz, the champion of pictorial and artistic photography. Robert Demachy's work had a strong public following and he achieved a good deal of acclaim for his artistic photographic interpetations. Demachy was the author of many articles on photography and on the pictorialist movement. He ceased his involvement in photography abruptly in 1914 without offering any reason for doing so.

DONNADIEU

Professor of Zoology at the Faculty of Science, University of Lyon. Donnadieu was the author of numerous books and articles on photography. He made several important discoveries in photographic technique including the use of silver bromide impregnated gelatin film and the development of techniques for animated photography. He was the author of the book *Science and Saint Suaire of Turin* (1903).

DUCOS DU HAURON, Louis 1837–1920

When Ducos du Hauron was 25 years old, he submitted a paper entitled *A method for the photographic reconstruction of colours by 3 filter separation of light and triple reversal printing*, to Mons Lelut, Membre de l'Institut. Ducos du Hauron had the idea of taking 3 black and white negatives of a subject using three different colour filters, red, yellow and blue, and subsequently printing three superimposed positives on tinted gelatin paper. The process Ducos du Hauron described was theoretical and he never produced any colour photographs by

this method. He initiated the use of collodion to obtain the first trichrome photographic images in 1868, and patented this process on November 22 of the same year. On May 7, 1869, the record of this discovery was presented to the French Photographic Society; curiously on the same day, Charles Cros described an identical process to the Society. The question of priority for the discovery of the process was courteously resolved between the two inventors. The genius of Louis Ducos du Hauron allowed him not only to foreshadow the colour photographic printing process by colour separation but also the production of colour transparencies for projection using three colour separated images, violet, orange and green. As well, he invented a colour printing process used in automated photographic printing. He perfected the heliochrome-carbon process in 1870 in which Blanquart-Evrard and Gustave Pereire were involved. In 1878 the German photographer Albert offered to exploit the heliochrome-carbon process commercially in partnership with Ducos du Hauron, but he refused on account of his patriotic feelings against the Germans following France's defeat in the 1870 war. In 1884 Alexandre Jaillie d'Agen invested capital with Ducos du Hauron to commercialise the carbon-heliochrome process. He hired a talented photocalligrapher, Quinsac, to help in the enterprise. The business failed; the factory was destroyed by fire and Jaillie and Quinsac both died shortly after. When Ducos du Hauron's patent expired he asked the French Government to extend it. The request was refused and he lost all the commercial advantage of an invention which was to make fortunes for others. Discouraged, Ducos du Hauron left France in 1884 to go to Algeria where he lived with his brother and ran a small photographic studio. He returned to France in 1896 and in 1907. In partnership with his nephew, he contracted to market Omnicolour plates made by Jougla. The partnership between Lumière and Jougla put paid to any hopes Ducos du Hauron had of seeing one of his discoveries commercialised for his own financial gain. He died in 1920 in Agen, where he had gone to live with a relative. His obituary reported 'Monsieur Ducos du Hauron died in Agen, his birthplace at the age of 83 in extreme poverty. The Administrators of the Departments of Lot and Garonne and the town of Agen had recently voted to provide a modest pension to Mons Ducos du Hauron. Unfortunately, their generous gesture came too late'.

EMERSON, Peter Henry 1856–1936

Born in Cuba of English and American parents, Emerson grew up and lived in England, devoting himself to photography. Between 1885 and 1900 Emerson started the 'naturalistic' School of photography as a response to the School of 'artistic' photography established by Rejlander and Henry Peach Robinson. He published a book entitled *Naturalistic Photography for students of the Art* (1889) in which he developed his theories on photography as a creative art.

FENTON, Roger 1819–1869

English barrister and photographer, Foundation member of the French Photographic Society and Secretary of the Royal Photographic Society of London. Fenton studied painting in France under Louis Delaroche and Gustave Le Gray. One of the first war photographers, Fenton was commissioned by Queen Victoria to cover the Crimean war from February to June 1855. He developed his collodion plate photographs in the field often under enemy fire. His war photographs created

IMAGES; ILLUSION AND REALITY

a great stir at the World Fair of 1855, particularly one panel of photographs made up of 11 views depicting a panorama of windmills between the English and French army sectors. Fenton photographed the English countryside extensively and his pictures of the ruins of old abbeys and castles in Great Britain and Ireland were featured in a book published in 1862.

FIERLANTS, Edmond 1819–1869
Belgian photographer, Foundation member of the French Photographic Society. Fierlants learnt photography from Hippolyte Bayard in Paris and founded the Royal Belgian Photographic Society. In 1860 he received a grant from the Belgian government to photograph the monuments of Anvers, Brussels, Bruges and Louvain. Fierlants specialized in architectural photography and in photographing works of art. In 1867 he photographed the works of Antoine Wiertz, a Belgian painter (1806–1865). Fierlant's photographs were reproduced in large format up to a size of 1.45 metres. In 1865, he published a book of his work which included 1500 photographs.

FRANCK de VILLECHOLLE, Alexander 1816–1906
Villecholle began his career in literature but was carried away by a passion for photography and in particular for the Daguerreotype. He emigrated to Barcelona in Spain returning to France in 1853 after Napoleon III became Emperor. He set up a studio in Paris in the rue Vivienne and became a fashionable photographic portrait artist. He was also a lecturer in photography at the école Centrale des Arts et Manufactures and at the école Polytechnique. Villecholle played an active part in the affairs of the French Photographic Society.

GIMPEL, Louis
Member of the French Photographic Society, Gimpel was a professional photographer who began the journal *Illustrated Life* in 1900. In 1904, he joined the staff of the publication *Illustration* for which he did the colour photography. On June 10, 1907 he organised a public seminar for Louis Lumière to present the details of his 'Autochrome' process for the first time. Much later in 1932 Gimpel organized a 25th anniversary celebration of Lumière's discovery at the premises of the French Photographic Society. He participated in many of the Society's activities and kept an historical record of the many events and developments of the autochrome process e.g. aerial pictures taken from a balloon in 1908 with available light, autochrome reproductions, the enhancement of the sensitivity of autochrome plates and so forth. Gimpel gave a total of 23 papers to the French Photographic Society, and 28 lectures on photography in France and overseas. In his professional capacity he contributed to about 50 French and foreign journals. On his death, part of his photographic collection was given to the French Photographic Society by his family.

GREEN, John Buckley 1832–1856
Member of the French Photographic Society. Green was an American archaeologist who lived in France. He was authorised by Saïd Pacha to do some excavations at Medine Habou in Upper Egypt. Green brought back from this digging 200 Calotype negatives made on dry waxed paper. Blanquart-Evrard chose prints from a hundred of these photographs for a book entitled. *The Nile — Monuments — Explorations.* This book appeared in 1854 under Green's authorship. A small

book on Egyptian hieroglyphics comprising 11 lithographs and 11 pages of text was published by Firmin Didot in 1855 with the title *Excavations undertaken at Thebes in 1855, hieroglyphic texts and unedited documents.* These are the only surviving works of this talented photographer. Green died at the age of 27.

HARIHARAN, P. 1926– .
Hariharan was born in India and was Director of the Laboratories at Hindustan Photo Films and Professor at the Indian Institute of Science, Bangalore, before coming to Australia in 1973. He is at present a Senior Principal Research Scientist at the Division of Applied Physics of the CSIRO. Hariharan has made significant contributions in interferometry and holography and has been responsible for developing new techniques for multicolour holograms. He has more than 120 publications in international journals as well as a major review *Colour Holography* in *Progress in Optics.* He is also the author of two books, *Optical Holography* (Cambridge University Press, 1984) and *Optical Interferometry* (Academic Press, 1985). Hariharan is a Fellow of the Optical Society of America, the Indian Academy of Science and the Indian National Academy of Science. He was on the Editorial Board of *Optica Acta* from 1973 to 1979, and is currently on the Editorial Board of *Optics Letters.* He has been Chairman of the Australian National Committee for Optics from 1979 and was elected Vice President of the International Commission for Optics in August 1984.

HEILMANN, J.J.
Foundation member of the French Photographic Society. Heilmann was born in Mulhouse and began his photography at Pau working later with Maxwell Lyte and Stewart. He was one of the first photographers to be involved in photographic enlargement. In 1853, Heilmann invented a device which enabled negative images to be either enlarged or reduced.

HUMBERT DE MOLARD, Louis Adolphe 1800–1874
Foundation member of the French Photographic Society. Humbert de Molard was a gentleman farmer who came from a family with a military background. He practised photography actively from 1843 to 1860. His interest in photography seems to have been connected with his second marriage (his first wife having died in 1840). Humbert de Molard concentrated first on the Daguerreotype then later on the Calotype, working with Henriette Renée Patu, a talented artist of miniatures and a significant property owner near Lagny. Humbert de Molard was fascinated by chemistry and with his knowledge of this science he was well suited to take part in those committees set up to examine new photographic processes presented to the French Photographic Society. He was frequently asked to try out many of the new techniques and to report on them in the bulletin of the Society. Methods for toning negatives with gold salts, methods using salts of uranium, collodion processes and so on were all subjects of Humbert de Molard's photographic experiments, the results of which enriched the collections of the French Photographic Society and its journal. The role played by Humbert de Molard in the history of photography was not just that of an inventor but more importantly, that of a catalyst and of an artist of consummate sensitivity.

JEUFFRAIN, Paul 1808–1896
A draper from Louviers, Paul Jeuffrain had been a naval officer in his youth. He was a member of the French

Photographic Society from 1855 until his death. In 1913 his son, who was also a member of the French Photographic Society, donated all his father's photographic works to the Society. These works comprised all the Calotypes Jeuffrain made during his journeys to Italy in 1852 and to Algeria in 1856.

LE GRAY, Gustave 1820–1882

Foundation member of the French Photographic Society. One of the many painters who derived great satisfaction from photography as an art form. Le Gray exhibited his paintings in art salons between 1848 and 1853 and he played an active part in photographic circles in Paris during this time, mainly through the French Photographic Society. His work centred principally on improvements to negative papers, particularly in regard to enhancing their sensitivity and their utility. Le Gray recommended the use of collodion in paper negative preparation in 1849; subsequently he invented the dry waxed negative paper. In 1851 he was commissioned by the French Government to photograph sites and monuments of the Touraine and Aquitaine regions of France in collaboration with Mestral. His particular talents enabled him to introduce several famous persons to photography. Adrien Tournachon, the brother of Nadar, Charles Nègre and Henri le Secq were all pupils of Le Gray. Le Gray set up business at 35 rue des Capucines, in the same building as Nadar. Le Gray did not succeed in becoming one of the fashionable society photographers at the time when the 'visiting card' portraiture was all the rage. His business failed to flourish and it is thought that he moved to Cairo where he died in 1882.

LORENT, August Jakob 1813–1884

Lorent was born in the United States, and his parents emigrated to south-west Germany when he was 4 years old. He studied Botany and Zoology at the University of Heidelberg. He was greatly influenced by the work of Alexander von Humbold and Aimé Bonpland. At the age of 29 Lorent travelled to the near East, first to Istanbul then to Egypt returning to Jerusalem by way of the Red Sea. He published a book in 1845 entitled *Journeys through the Orient 1842–1843*. Lorent discovered nine new species of plants on his travels and described these in his book but made no mention at all of photography. However, it is certain that on these journeys Lorent took photographs of monuments and other examples of the local cultures and civilizations. The monuments of the Pharoahs — the ruins of Saracen — the Greek temples were subjects to which he subsequently devoted his life. Lorent's photographs were of a very large size (38 x 47 cm — 45 x 60 cm and even 45 x 102 cm). They had a great success when exhibited at contemporary photographic shows. Lorent worked from negatives made on dry waxed paper and his pictures needed around three hours exposure time. The subsequent laboratory procedures took some 37 hours involving 9 different processes.

LYTE, Farnham Maxwell 1828–1906

Member of the French Photographic Society. He was an Englishman who, in spite of his delicate health, lived to 78 years of age. He spent most of his life in France in the Midi and in the Pyrenees. He submitted a paper to the French Photographic Society about the results of his researches on a dry collodion process.

Lyte specialised in photographing the skies. Scenic photographs up until this time showed skies totally devoid of clouds because the low order of sensitivity of the emulsions could not record their images against the sun light. Lyte took many photographs of the skies showing clouds and then superimposed these on other pictures to provide a more natural effect. This artificial practice was, of course, rejected by the purists who accepted only unretouched photographs.

MALIN, David 1941– .

Malin was born in England and trained as a chemist. He worked for many years with optical and electronmicroscopes before turning his attention to larger and more distant things in Australia. He works at the Siding Spring Mountain Observatory and at the Anglo-Australian Observatory's Laboratories in Sydney. Malin's background in chemistry has helped him to develop the complicated hypersensitising photographic processes which have given enormous gains in speed to the special photographic plates used in astronomy. Malin has developed new ways of extracting information from astronomical plates, which have given him a world-wide reputation. These novel image enhancement techniques have led to the discovery of some extremely faint but large-scale features associated with otherwise normal galaxies. These are some of the faintest images ever detected by an earth-based telescope and represent the state of the art in faint object detection as well as being a major contribution to research on elliptical galaxies. He has recently developed a unique process for making colour photographs of extremely faint astronomical objects which is revealing some new and important astrophysical data. The colours in the photographs tell directly of the often complicated interplay between the absorption, scattering, reflection and emission of light at enormous distances and are in many cases the first colour pictures to reveal these effects. Malin has written many scientific papers and popular articles on astronomy and photography and is a well-known lecturer on these topics. He was co-author with Paul Murdin and David Allen of the *Catalogue of the Universe* and with Paul Murdin *The Colours of the Stars* both published by the Cambridge University Press. Malin's contributions to photography have been recognised by his election as a Fellow of the Royal Photographic Society and his work in astronomy by the award of the Gwilt-Jackson medal of the Royal Astronomical Society. In 1985 he was a recipient of Henri Chretien award of the American Astronomical Society.

MEADE Brothers

The Meade brothers were Americans. In 1848, after spending time in Paris they asked Daguerre if they could take his portrait. All in all they made some 7 or 8 portraits of the celebrated inventor. The French Photographic Society has two of these portraits and two others exist in America in private collections.

MIGURSKI, Charles

Member of the French Photographic Society. Migurski founded the Photographic Society of Odessa in 1858. The President was Count Michel Tolstoi. Migurski regularly exhibited his works and reported on his photographic techniques. These reports were later published in the bulletin of the French Photographic Society. He was the author of the book entitled *A Short Course in Photographic Chemistry* and another treatise on the practise of photography published in 1859 in Odessa.

MOESSARD, O.

Member of the French Photographic Society. Moessard was

attached to the Geographic service of the French Army. He perfected the 'Cylindrographe', an apparatus which allowed panoramas to be recorded over a range of 170°. This apparatus was particularly useful for wide field topographic photography. Moessard also invented the 'Tourniquet' apparatus which was used experimentally in photography around 1889. Moessard was greatly interested in aerial photography and took pictures from a balloon in 1888.

MUYBRIDGE, Eadweard James 1830–1904
Muybridge was born in England and emigrated to the United States where he became a photographer. His early work was in industrial photography but he also took some of the earliest pictures of the area that was to become the Yosemite National Park in California. He was interested particularly in the study of human and animal movement and concentrated on this aspect of photography from 1872–1885. His work published in 1887 comprised 781 plates which recorded observations on the dissection of movements of both man and animals. With these photographic analyses Muybridge showed that the way painters and draftsmen had depicted the gait of horses was false. For his studies on the analysis of movement in horses Muybridge used 24 cameras placed side by side; their shutters were held open by a cord which was broken by the passage of the horse automatically releasing the shutters of the cameras. The horse's movements were recorded at shutter speeds of 1/500 of a second.

NADAR, Paul 1856–1940
Member of the French Photographic Society. The only son of Gaspard Félix Tournachon, alias Nadar, Paul Nadar was introduced to photography at a very young age. His career suffered because of the great distinction and personality of his father. In 1887 when he was 31 years old he was given the responsibility of managing the family photographic business. Although Paul Nadar had both initiative and foresight he was not a good business man. He knew that the photographic industry would expand enormously and that photographic studios would disappear quickly or at least decrease in number because of the growth in the number of amateur photographers. He also envisaged the establishment of photographic supply houses and centres for mass produced photography. 'One is less disposed to put money into photography today than previously because most people now know what photography is all about; one's friends are always telling you the price of plates and paper'. Paul Nadar knew that photography was entering its first commercial period (he was the agent for Eastman Kodak in France in 1891) and that the artistic photograph would become less important. However it is also clear that in spite of Paul Nadar's commercial perceptiveness, he never knew how to manage his financial affairs satisfactorily or to exercise proper control of the family business which was made over to him by his father in 1895. Paul Nadar founded a magazine *Paris Photographer* (1891–1894) and took a very active part in the promotion and organization of photography and in the commercial exploitation of his father's work.

NADAR, Jeune. Tournachon, Adrien 1825–1903
Member of the French Photographic Society, the younger brother of Gaspard Félix Tournachon. Adrien seemed destined to live in the shadow of his famous brother. He worked professionally under the pseudonym of Nadar Jeune. He was one of 15 designers and photographers employed on Nadar's Panthéon and he made a significant contribution to its success. The idea for the Panthéon belonged to Adrien's brother. The work was a collection of a large number of photographic caricatures of prominent people of the day and it was widely acclaimed when it appeared first in Paris. Adrien learned photography from the celebrated Gustave Le Gray. He set up his photographic studio first in the bd des Capucines and then in 1854 at 133 rue St Lazare. There was confusion over the authorship of photographs signed by Adrien under his pseudonym 'Nadar Jeune'. He brought an action against his elder brother who signed his work 'Nadar' to preserve the exclusive use of his particular pseudonym. His professional career as a photographer was short; he suffered from poor health and from 1890 until his death he spent much of his life in hospital.

NADAR, Tournachon, Gaspard Félix 1820–1910
Gaspard Félix Tournachon was a writer, editor, caricaturist and photographer of great distinction and accomplishment who left an indelible mark on photographic art and technology. The story of his life reads like a romantic novel; he was involved with the press, with politics during the reign of Napoleon III and he was implicated in most of the radical movements in politics of his time.

Félix Tournachon was the grandson and son of printers. He was obliged, because of family circumstances, to help in the family business at an early age. His father died in 1887, leaving the family Printery destitute and his mother without resources. In 1838, at the age of 18 he went to Paris with several letters of introduction accompanied by his mother and brother Adrien aged 13 years who was in delicate health. It was from this time that his real journalistic career began. He got a job with the *Journal of Women and Fashion* and in a few months he had become the official theatre critic for the *Revue and Gazette of the Theatre*. In 1839, he started up his own journal called *The Negotiator* followed soon by a second called *The Audience*. Both of these were legal journals dealing with the law and with court proceedings. Nadar became involved in the Bohemian life style of Paris and was part of a group of unknown artists who, like members of the new socialist movement, were hassled continuously by the state police of Napoleon III.

In 1841 Tournachon took the pseudonym of Nadar, the name which became the trade mark of his photographic works. This alias carried on a familiar tradition amongst artists of the period who took names ending in 'dar'. It was in this way that Tournachon became Tournadar, and was then shortened by omitting the Tour to give Nadar. In 1849 Nadar collaborated in the production of *A Journal of Laughs* which had a print run of up to 14 000 copies of which 8000 were bought by subscribers. This was the beginning of his career as a caricaturist. Nadar's drawings were often slanted against the government of Napoleon III. He was responsible for an idea which he called 'Nadar's Panthéon' which brought together in one lithograph caricatures of 300 of the most celebrated individuals of the period. It required 15 artists to complete the work and 800 drawings were produced, many of them by Nadar himself. Some of the identities caricaturized in the lithograph were Theophile Gautier, Vigny, Hugo, Balzac, Lamartine, Musset as well as other famous authors of the period, many of whom were still living at the time. Nadar used photography to help him develop certain of his caricatures, notably those of Vigny, Balzac & Delacroix. There is no doubt that one can find certain similarities between the drawings Nadar made in 1858 and his photography of the same era. In 1854, Nadar set himself up in a photographic studio at 113 rue Saint Lazare. Naturally enough, many of the personalities who were featured in the Panthéon became Nadar's clients. Between 1856 and 1859 Nadar took his best portrait photographs. His pictures of Sarah Bernhardt and other celebrities were characterized by 'naturalness', an effect achieved by Nadar posing his subjects without artificial props. He said 'Photography is a marvellous discovery; it is a science which occupies the greatest minds, an art which hones the wisest intellects, and a technology which can be used by the most veritable fool.'

Nadar, was fascinated with ballooning; his first ascent in a navigable balloon was in 1857 and in 1858 he took the first aerial photograph. In the same year, he took the first photographs by artificial light. Aeronautics continued to fascinate Nadar throughout his life and in the event ruin him financially. He ran a Company of Military Aerobatics during the 1870 Franco-Prussian war making several reconnaissance trips in his balloons. He organised an aerial postal service in Paris during the German siege to transport mail to the besieged Parisiens. In 1874, Nadar organised, in the main salon of his sumptuous studio in the bd des Capucines, the first Impressionist Exhibition. Under the title of 'The Anonymous Society of Artists, Painters, Sculptors, and Engravers', the exhibition brought together the works of Monet, Pissaro, Renoir, Sisley, Cézanne, Dégas and Boudin. Again in 1878 Nadar organised an exhibition dedicated to the work of Daumier, at a time when the artist was in dire financial straights. A man of talent, with many facets to his personality, generous of heart, always ready to become involved in particular causes, Nadar had a difficult old age and end to his life. In 1887 his wife became partly paralyzed and he left his business to his son Paul retiring to the outskirts of Paris. Paul was not able to manage the financial affairs of the business and Nadar had to return to Paris in 1894 to redress the family's delicate financial situation. These problems led to a continuing conflict between father and son and subsequently Nadar decided to leave Paris and to live in Marseilles (September 1897). Nadar was obliged to sell all his assets progressively to support himself. In 1900, a retrospective exhibition of his work was presented at the World Fair. He published his memoirs in a book entitled 'When I was a photographer'. Nadar died in 1910, and Georges Grappe said of him: 'He had so much life, was so generous and of such nobility of spirit that all of us who had the honour of knowing this grand old man, hoped that he would never die'.

NEGRE, Charles

Member of the French Photographic Society. Nègre was a painter who was introduced to photography by Le Gray in 1851. He used photography to provide the subject material for his paintings. These were of 'genre' subjects and close copies of the photographs. He achieved a great deal of notoriety for his pictures which were exhibited successfully at the Salon. One particular photograph and painting entitled *The organ grinder* became very well known. Nègre used the calotype process and refined his photographic techniques to enable him to produce instantaneous shots. In 1852 Nègre photographed the monuments of the French Midi where he was born. The photographic printers, Fonteny, produced an edition of Nègre's picture collection under the title *Midi de la France*. The edition was not a success because of the high cost of each print (8 francs) and because the prints were unstable and faded. This was a problem which bedevilled all photographers of this period and Nègre attempted to find a solution to it by heliography. He employed the technique with bitumen of Judea which had been developed originally by Nicéphore Nièpce, using gold with it according to the method of Fizeaul (1840). When the French Photographic Society arranged the concours for the Duc de Luynes prize Nègre submitted his prints to the judging panel but his entry was discounted because he was not able to provide sufficient detail of the method to enable his results to be reproduced by other photographers or to be used commercially. In the event Poitevin carried off the prize. In spite of this the Duc de Luynes intended to have Nègre's photographs, which he had taken on his trip to the Holy Land, engraved. Unfortunately the Duc died before the project was undertaken. Nègre retired to Nice where he worked as a lecturer in design and drafting. He died in 1880.

NIEPCE, Joseph Nicéphore 1765–1833

Born at Chalon-sur Saône, died at Saint Loup le Varenna. Joseph Nièpce was the discoverer of photography and with his brother Claude, invented the Pyreolophore, an internal combustion engine, for which they took out a patent in 1807 and for which Claude, until his death, tried vainly to commercialise. In 1813, Nicéphore Nièpce became interested in lithography. He tried to fix images obtained with the camera obscura on sheets of paper sensitized with silver chloride fixed in nitric acid. He obtained some negatives on paper in this way but the discovery led him completely astray and diverted his research for some time into unproductive directions. In 1822 he reproduced some contact translucent engravings by using glass plates coated with bitumen of Judea. The solubility of the bitumen in the presence of lavender oil is changed by exposure to light. The prints Nièpce obtained by this process were called heliographs and could be reproduced by an engraving technique. Through the good offices of Charles Chevalier, a Paris Optician, Nièpce came to know Daguerre and started corresponding with him, a correspondence marked by suspicion on the part of Nièpce and curiosity on the part of Daguerre. They met first in 1827, when Nièpce passed through Paris on his way back from London after visiting his brother Claude who was very ill. While in England Nièpce submitted his discovery to the Royal Society but the Society turned down his communication for lack of detail. Nièpce on his return to France went through a difficult time. His brother died insane, and Nièpce's personal fortune had been largely dissipated by his unproductive research. On December 14, 1829 he signed a provisional joint partnership agreement with Daguerre. Nièpce contributed for his share of the partnership, his discoveries in photography while Daguerre offered the refinements which he had made to the camera obscura, his talents, and his industry. It was rather an unequal contribution. Nièpce died in 1833 and his son Isidore who succeeded him, signed the definitive contract on June 13, 1837. Nièpce's name was not associated with the Daguerreotype when Arago publicly announced the discovery of the process on August 19, 1839.

Nièpce also invented the iris diaphram and the extendable camera bellows but received no credit for these inventions. These discoveries played a significant part subsequently in photographic development.

IMAGES; ILLUSION AND REALITY

PERSONNAZ, Antonin
Member of the French Photographic Society. Personnaz was a great lover of art and a personal friend of Pissaro. He was commissioned by the painter Bonnat, a friend of his father, to establish an art museum at Bayonne containing the famous painter's collection of objets d'art which he had accumulated, together with his paintings, during his life. He was rewarded by the Legion d'Honneur for this work. From his youth Personnaz had been associated with the Impressionist painters and he bought many of their paintings. He was able to do this because of his special financial circumstances and as a consequence he had a splendid collection of the works of Berthe Morisot, Claude Monet, Guillaumin and of course, Pissaro, whom he knew particularly well. This collection is now at the Musée de l'Orangerie in Paris. Personnaz bequeathed his collection to the Louvre on his death. Personnaz gave seminars to the French Photographic Society on the aesthetics of black and white photography which were extremely well received and very popular. These talks were evidence of Personnaz's artistic talent and of his highly cultivated mind. Personnaz worked with Lumière autochrome plates to produce effects with colour and light. These were the feelings and images that were expressed in paintings of his Impressionist colleagues. Personnaz used a variety of special masking techniques and varying exposure times to produce the special effects in his photographs.

POITEVIN, Alphonse
Chemical engineer, elected a member of the French Photographic Society in 1860. Poitevin became involved in photography almost from the time it was discovered. He perfected a method of obtaining an engraving from the daguerreotype image and gave a paper to the Academie des Sciences in 1848 on this discovery. He was convinced of the significant advantages of using gelatin as a base for photographic plates and in 1851 he developed gelatin glass plates coated with silver salts. He took advantage of the imperviousness and water repellant properties of gelatin bichromate when it is exposed to light, and perfected the 'Helioplastie' process by which replicas were made from bichromate gelatin prints. On the 27 August 1855 Poitevin took out two patents, domestically and overseas. The first was for the 'Helioplastie' process. This patent was contested publicly by Pretsch. The second patent was for a process of making ink impressions on paper or on stone. These two inventions earned him a gold medal in the Duc de Luyne's exhibition in 1859 and a second medal, in 1862, with a prize of 2000 francs. Poitevin hoped to commercialise his discoveries and he opened an automated photographic printery in the rue Saint Jacques. He made this business over to Lemercier in 1857.

PRETSCH, Paul 1808–1873
Printer, born in Vienna. Pretsch became director of the Imperial Printery of Vienna in 1842 and devoted himself to research into the photosensitivity of the organic bichromates.

He invented a photo-mechanical printing process and set up a business in London. In 1856 in collaboration with Roger Fenton he founded 'The Photo-Galvano-Graphic Company'. The company published between November 1856 and September 1857 six photographic editions under the title

Photographic art treasures and art illustrated by art and nature. Although not a member of the French Photographic Society, Pretsch had regular contact with the Society from 1856–1864

In 1863 he left London and returned to Vienna to his previous position at the Imperial Printery.

PUYO, Emile Joachim Camille 1857–1933
Puyo came from an upper-middle class family and was educated at the école Polytechnique and at the Military Academy. He rose to field rank in the French army. Puyo was gifted in drawing and painting and he was captivated by photography. In 1902 he quit the army to devote himself to photographic art. He was a member of the Photo Club of Paris and became a close friend of Robert Demachy. Their names were inevitably linked with the French pictorialist movement. Puyo made use of all the methods and techniques which were successfully exploited in pictorialism; gum bichromate plates, transfer processes and effects obtained by special lenses to give diffused light and soft focus. After the Photo-Club was disbanded in 1914, Puyo directed a number of photographic workshops at the Photographic Society and produced numerous articles on photographic techniques and photographic art.

RÉGNAULT, Henri Victor 1810–1878
Foundation member of the French Photographic Society and its first President from 1855 to 1868. Régnault was a chemist and physicist, Professor at the Collège de France and Director of the Manufactory at Sèvres.

He was elected a member of the Academie des Sciences and became a Professor of Physics at the Collège de France at age 31. He discovered vinyl chloride in 1835, and carbon tetrachloride in 1839.

In 1851 he joined the Heliographic Society and while working on the chemistry of photographic developers he discovered that the developing properties of pyrogallic acid were superior to those of gallic acid which was the developing agent in use at the time.

As President of the Photographic Society until 1868 he showed great vision in all matters concerning the Society and its future. He was responsible for setting up the photographic collection of the Society and establishing the museum of photography, the library and a testing laboratory. He organised and drafted the regulations for Duc de Luynés competition in 1856; the results of this competition were of great significance to the graphic arts because of the advent of automated photographic procedures. In 1873 while the honorary President of the Society Régnault advocated the need for a common nomenclature for photography. Régnault was a brilliant scientist, an excellent photographer and a man ahead of his time in his conception of the pictorial image and photographic artistry.

REJLANDER, Oscar Gustave 1813–1875
A Swedish citizen and painter who lived in Great Britain. Rejlander began photography in 1840, and was influenced throughout his life by pictorial and visual experiences and culture. He approached photography like a painter. His work centred around 'allegorical' photographs, one of which was *The Two Ways of Life*, a composite photographic montage made of 30 negatives. This allegory which depicts a young man torn between virtue and sin was considered one of the monuments of artistic photography of the day.

ROBINSON, Henry Peach 1830–1901
English painter.

Like Rejlander, Robinson practised photography from the viewpoint of a painter. His compositions reflected the pictorial culture which underlay his family and his background. Robinson produced two books dedicated to photographic art: *Pictorial Effect in Photography* (1869) and *Photography* (1884).

ROUSSEAU, Louis 1811–1874
Rousseau was the son of an employee in the animal house of the Museum of Natural History in Paris. He began work at the age of 17 in the Zoology laboratory of this institution. He was a competent employee and was promoted in 1834 to a laboratory assistantship. He worked for close on 40 years for the Professor of Malacology and Zoophytology at the museum. He took part in various study tours to the Crimea, to the Seychelles, Madagascar, Iceland and Greenland. He was one of the first to produce scientific illustrations by photography. In 1853 he had the idea of publishing 10 original zoological manuscripts. He presented this project to the Academie des Sciences and received a grant of 2000 francs. The question of conserving the photographs caused members of the Academy some concern and it was decided to ask the publisher to reproduce the photographs as printed plates. Rousseau used the process that Nièpce de Saint Victor had reported to the Academie des Sciences in May 1853. Nièpce de Saint Victor had refined the heliographic process of his cousin Nicéphore Nièpce, making some important improvements to it. *Zoological Photography* is one of the first scientific publications illustrated by an automated printing process. Although Rousseau foreshadowed publishing 10 volumes, he only managed, in the end, to publish 3.

SALZMANN, Auguste 1824–1872
French archaeologist and painter. Born in Alsace, Salzmann left his native province when 33 and lived in Paris on and off for the rest of his life. In 1847, after a trip to Italy, he exhibited 3 paintings at the Salon de Paris — 'Souvenir of Ischia' — 'The Gulf of Naples' and 'View of the Temples of Phaestos'. In 1848, he visited Algeria accompanied by the painter Eugène Fromentin. The following year Salzmann exhibited two of his photographic works in Paris, 'The Outskirts of Elksour, on the edge of the Sahara' and 'Interior court of a jewish house in Constantine'. During the years 1851–1853, he became interested in archaeology and joined an archaeological expedition to Greece. In 1854, he travelled to Jerusalem and took over 200 excellent Calotype photographs which Blanquart-Evrard subsequently published in his famous photographic printing house. The two volume luxury edition was entitled *Jerusalem études et reproductions photographiques des monuments de la Ville Sainte.*

SCHOEFL, Gutta
Fellow, Australian National University. Dr Schoefl has done research into the ultrastructure and functional attributes of blood capillaries and blood cells in laboratories in Boston, Paris, Oxford and Canberra. Her interest in the plastic arts and in the physiological implications of form and function led her to investigate the plastic deformation imposed on lymphocytes as they cross the blood capillary membrane. Her researches provided the definitive analysis of the mode of egress of these cells from blood vessels and demonstrated the structural arrangements of the cells within the capillary wall that allow this phenomenon to occur. Dr Schoefl's artistic interpretations of ultrastructural detail, her analysis of microscopic vascular patterns in terms of recognisable analogies and her electromicroscopic caricatures have given both novelty and authenticity to the microscopic world.

SILVY, Camille
Member of the French Photographic Society. Silvy was a diplomat who abandoned the service to set up a photographic studio in London in 1858. His studio was patronized by the Royal Family and by the English aristocracy. In 1860, he brought out a photographic reproduction of a magazine entitled *Sforza*. Following on this work Silvy planned to reproduce photographically the 'palimpsestes'* of the Vatican. He invented a method for restoring faded texts before reproducing them photographically. He was also interested in panoramic photography and the French Photographic Society has in its collection a Calotype composed of several negatives representing the Rond Point de l'Etoile.

* *Palimpseste:* A manuscript on parchment; the writing can be erased so that the parchment can be reused.

STEWART, John
Member of the French Photographic Society. English photographer who worked in the Pyrenees with Heilmann and Maxwell-Lyte. Stewart was the brother-in-law of John Frederick Herschel (1792–1871) the English scholar who invented the spectroscopic analysis of light waves and discovered infra-red radiation.

TALBOT, William Henry Fox 1800–1878
Born in Lacock, England, Talbot is considered to be, with Nièpce and Daguerre, one of the inventors of photography. Talbot showed in 1835 that by placing plants and flowers on a sheet of paper sensitised with silver salts, he could obtain a negative image. However he could not fix these images. On the other hand, as soon as he pressed this negative onto another sheet of sensitized paper he was able to obtain a positive image. This discovery remains the essence of the contemporary photographic process. Talbot persued his research for some years without divulging his results to anyone. It was the announcement of Daguerre's discovery in 1839 by Arago that forced Talbot to communicate his findings to the Royal Society on 31st January 1839. He called his process the Calotype (Greek — Kalos, beautiful). The Calotype allowed a negative image to be used to reproduce an unlimited number of photographic positives. In contrast Daguerre's invention gave a single image which was not reproducible. In 1853 Talbot published his work on photographic engraving using bichromate gelatin. Poitevin and those interested in photomechanical methods developed their ideas later from this discovery by Talbot. Talbot was also a distinguished archaeologist and linguist. He published several important books on archaeology, on language and on photography.